W9-DHI-905

THE NEW PARENTS' MAGAZINE BABY CARE BOOK

A Mother's Guide to the First Six Years

by Eleanor S. Duncan

with the counsel of the Editor of Parents' Magazine

Mrs. Mary E. Buchanan

and a Medical and Health Section

by Dr. Dorothy V. Whipple, Pediatrician

formerly with the United States Children's Bureau

PARENTS' MAGAZINE ENTERPRISES, INC.

PUBLISHERS OF PARENTS' MAGAZINE

52 VANDERBILT AVENUE, NEW YORK

THE NEW PARENTS' MAGAZINE BABY CARE BOOK

Library of Congress Catalog Card Number: 63-14093
Printed in the United States of America

1965

Parents' Magazine Books

BABY CARE BOOK

FAMILY COOKBOOK

GUIDING YOUR CHILD

FAMILY HEALTH

Foreword

This is a warm, friendly, wonderfully helpful book written by a mother for other mothers. It contains the wisdom that comes from experience, based on a thorough grounding in child development, child feeding, child guidance, parent-child relationships.

Parents' Magazine has always believed in parents. In an era of "experts" on bringing up children, *Parents' Magazine* has always insisted that parents, too, should be numbered among the experts. There is something about having a child or two that tests theories and research findings as nothing else can. That's why we asked the extremely intelligent young mother of two children to write this book.

Eleanor Duncan tells simply, concretely how she uses the new knowledge of child care, adapting it to meet her children's particular needs and her family's way of living. We know that other mothers will find her experience and her suggestions warmly helpful.

When it came to health, we asked Dr. Dorothy V. Whipple, formerly with the United States Children's Bureau, now in the private practice of pediatrics, and the mother of three children, to contribute a section. We believe that the reader will discover in that section all the things she most needs to know about the health care of babies and young children.

The delightful pictographs which illustrate this book in a gay and new way tell the story of child growth and give a preview of what to expect at various stages of development. Altogether, this book manages to give the expectant mother—whether expectant for the first time or not—all she needs to know. Above all, it says what every mother needs to feel if she and her baby are to be as happy as they can and should be: "This is wonderful—this having a baby! Don't let anyone get you to make hard work of it. It's something you'll be good at, too, if you learn all you can, trust your instincts, and enjoy your baby!"

MRS. MARY E. BUCHANAN, *Editor, Parents' Magazine*

Acknowledgment

What we know about bringing up children today—the methods, techniques, and theories on which the modern practice of child rearing is based—is the result of what has been found out about children in laboratories, clinics, in research studies by students of child development, by doctors, anthropologists, and educators. This book is firmly grounded on such a body of knowledge. I want to acknowledge my indebtedness to the following studies:

Those made by Wingate Todd at Western Reserve University; by Dr. Arnold Gesell and his coworkers at Yale University; the studies conducted under the direction of Dr. C. Anderson Aldrich at the Rochester Child Health Project; the work of Dr. Clara Davis in her experiments with child feeding; the findings of Dr. Sigmund Freud; the studies of growing children conducted at the Institute of Child Welfare of the University of California and at the Laboratory of Human Development at Harvard University; the researches carried out at the Child Welfare Research Station of Iowa University, at Teachers College, Columbia University, and at the University of Minnesota; the work carried on under the auspices of the United States Children's Bureau and the Extension Division of the United States Department of Agriculture; and other valuable contributions made by such groups as the Samuel Fels Research Institute at Antioch College and the Menninger Foundation, and by Dr. Alfred H. Washburn and his coworkers at the Child Research Council of the University of Colorado School of Medicine.

ELEANOR S. DUNCAN

Contents

How to use this book

This is a practical and *useful* book. You, as a parent, will refer to it many times for information, for reassurance, for guidance, for the answers to most of your questions. The book has been designed for easy reference and maximum usefulness. It is arranged in chronological order, from first signs of pregnancy to the growth and development of your child at six years of age. The table of contents lists all the subheadings for convenient reference. And the index—most useful tool of all—puts special emphasis on important subjects. Those of most vital interest are printed in bold type so that you can locate them quickly: such subjects as *Bathing*, *Clothing*, *Foods*, *Housework*, *Talking*, and many others. This is *your book*—may it serve you faithfully.

CHAPTER ONE

You're going to have a baby!

"We're going to have a baby!" When you've been wanting a baby and hoping for one, what more wonderful words can there be than these? Then, if you are like most of us, you begin to be intensely aware for the first time of everything you read and hear about bringing up children.

Aside from the joy you feel, you may also feel a little uncertain and even overwhelmed at the thought of being a parent. After all, it is a big responsibility. You've heard of all manner of problems and complexes that result if parents do the wrong thing. You realize the importance of the right kind of baby care, and the right start psychologically, but just what is right?

Prospective mothers all, *relax*. You couldn't have chosen a better time than now to have a baby. For years babies have been studied in the home, in clinics; their behavior patterns have been carefully noted, as well as their reactions to all sorts of situations and methods of handling. No matter what might come up between you and your baby, the authorities can help you.

Science offers the modern mother assistance and ready-made experience, which previous generations had to get for themselves, making many mistakes in the process. By drawing on the store of knowledge about baby care which has been amassed by experts, your way will be made much easier than if you had to operate entirely on a system of trial and error.

Accent on Love

At the same time, science is turning more and more toward the natural, instinctive ways of handling babies and children, with the accent on love and happiness in caring for your child. Mothers today are encouraged to cuddle the baby and enjoy him—something that was more or less frowned upon a generation ago. As you study and work with your own child, you will learn how best to apply the advice of science to his particular case. That is what is meant by using your own common sense, which the authorities want you to do. But we do have to know something about a subject before we can have much sense about it.

We urge you therefore to read and study and to avail yourself to the fullest extent of the new knowledge about the way children grow and develop. We assure you that it will remove many of the worries and superstitions that used to plague mothers. Then don't be afraid to revise and fit the advice to your own particular needs. Thus you will grow in skill and mother love, and soon become an expert in handling your own child.

For a Happy Pregnancy

One of the important discoveries of recent years has been the determination of the real role played by the mother's life during pregnancy in shaping the new baby. It has been firmly established that the more happy and serene the mother and the better care she gives herself, the sturdier and stronger the new baby is likely to be. All you have to think about for the present is this first step—a comfortable, happy pregnancy for yourself. And that is a matter of following a few simple rules.

Signs of Pregnancy

Very likely you are reasonably sure that you are pregnant or you would not be reading this, but it is a good idea to mention the symptoms here, since delayed menstruation alone is not a definite sign of pregnancy. Not all women experience nausea, but some do, usually in the morning. There is a tendency toward frequent urination; you may have to get up in the middle of the night. Some time after the first month, the breasts undergo changes, and you may find that they have become tender, even with tingling pains. They grow larger. The nipple area becomes brown, and a brown line may appear going south from the navel. If you are a brunet, you will notice the appearance of a network of blue veins near the surface of the skin of the breasts.

Choosing Your Doctor

If you have any of these symptoms, together or alone, you should see a doctor immediately. For a safe, normal pregnancy, it is important that you be under a doctor's care from the very first. He should be an obstetrician or a general practitioner who specializes in obstetrics. It is important to have a doctor you like, with whom you feel at ease.

Consult your dentist early in pregnancy and follow his recommendations for repairs and daily care of your teeth. To aid in the development of good teeth for your baby, some doctors prescribe fluoride pills. These should be started by the fourth month of pregnancy when the baby's teeth are developing in his gums.

The Medical Examination

You should have some idea in advance of what to expect in the doctor's office. He will ask you about your complete medical history. He will probably remove blood from a vein in your arm for a Wassermann test (obligatory in most states) and for other tests, such as blood type and determination of the Rh factor. He will take your blood pressure and will request a urine specimen.

Testing for Rh Factor

In recent years, much publicity has been given to the Rh factor, and perhaps you don't quite understand what it is. Part of the blood the doctor draws from you will be analyzed to see if your blood is Rh positive or negative. If it is positive, the doctor makes no more tests for this factor. But if you are Rh negative, he will want to analyze your husband's blood as well. If the baby's father proves to be Rh positive, there is a chance—but this is only about one chance in 100—that the baby's circulation may be affected adversely. When the doctor knows about this possibility beforehand, he can be prepared for any contingency that may arise. If this is your first baby, it is a comfort to know that the first-born rarely has any difficulty, even when the mother is Rh negative and the father Rh positive. It is in following pregnancies that special care must be exercised. But even in these cases, complications because of the Rh factor are the exception rather than the rule. Also, medical science is constantly perfecting its techniques for dealing with the Rh factor when it does make trouble. Those little drops of blood also tell the doctor the count of your red blood corpuscles and other things about your general bodily condition.

Further Examination

The doctor will examine your breasts and abdomen and take your external pelvic measurements. Next comes the internal examination. This examination is necessary and will not be uncomfortable if you relax completely. The baby has to pass between the pelvic bones, and the doctor must know whether the opening is large enough for a normal birth. In order to examine the uterus, he places two gloved fingers inside the vagina and his other hand on top of the abdomen. He can then note the size, shape, position, and consistency of your uterus and other pelvic organs. After the examination you will be given some general instructions.

Food Is Most Important

Your doctor will tell you how he wants you to conduct yourself throughout the months that the baby is forming. He will probably have a good deal to say about diet, for a well-balanced diet has been found to be one of the leading factors in avoiding complications, in ensuring safe deliveries, in producing fine infants.

For one thing, the doctor does not want you to put on too much weight. That will make you much more uncomfortable during pregnancy, will make it harder for the baby to be born, and the extra pounds will have to be lost later by laborious dieting. A twenty-pound gain during the entire pregnancy is the average allowance, and calories must be figured accordingly.

Another point is that the food you eat must supply the material for building your baby's body. Nature does her very best with whatever food materials are given her, but can do much better when provided with the right materials. It has been definitely proved that babies whose mothers have eaten ample protein, vitamin, and mineral foods during pregnancy are better specimens than those whose mothers have been short on these vital elements.

Keep the Calories Down

If your weight was normal at the time pregnancy began, your doctor will probably suggest that you keep to 2500 calories a day, the same as required for a moderately active non-pregnant woman. Your diet should be mainly meats, eggs, milk, vegetables, fruits, and whole-grain or fortified cereals and breads. If you can eat starches, sweets and fats and still keep your weight gain down, fine; but if you start gaining too fast, these are the foods to cut down on. Using skim milk instead of whole milk is a good way to reduce calories. If you are overweight to begin with, or underweight, he will specify diet adjustments accordingly. Your doctor must decide these things, and you should understand that there are urgent reasons for whatever dietary rules he gives you, including the vitamins he prescribes.

Importance of Liquids

He will ask you to drink about eight glasses of fluid a day. This is very important, for it helps the kidneys to carry the extra load pregnancy lays upon them. At least two of the glasses of fluid should be milk. Your daily milk requirement is one quart, part of which may be cooked. One ounce of unprocessed yellow cheese contains about the same food elements as one cup of milk.

Exercising

If you are healthy and normal, the doctor will probably permit you to indulge in your regular sports, with the provision that you don't overdo and become too tired. Remember that when a woman is pregnant, it takes much longer than at other times to get rested from exhaustion.

If you haven't gone in for sports, he will probably advise daily walks, starting with short ones and taking care not to wear yourself out. Ordinary household duties are good exercise, too. Just don't go in for bouts of wall washing or other strenuous activities that would tire you even if you were not pregnant.

Most women are drowsy during the early months of pregnancy and need extra sleep. Take an afternoon nap and go to bed early at night. If you have a job, try to arrange to lie down for ten minutes or so in the morning, at noon, and in the afternoon.

A Normal Social Life

Probably no one needs to tell a modern woman that it is proper to lead a completely normal life so far as social affairs and other outside activities are concerned, up to the door of the labor room. (A few alert souls actually manage to play a few hands of gin rummy with their husbands even at this stage.) Just make your excuses when you feel yourself growing weary. Pregnancy should be a happy state, and there is no reason in the world why you shouldn't go where you please and do the things that entertain you, so long as you get enough rest.

Your doctor, of course, will tell you at what intervals he wants you to come in to see him—usually every month until the end of pregnancy draws near, when some doctors like to see their patients every two weeks.

Ask the Doctor Before You Travel

An extensive trip should not be taken after the seventh month, unless you have your doctor's express permission. As a matter of fact, it is well to consult him before planning long trips at any time during pregnancy.

Medical science has made such enormous strides in making

labor safe for mother and child that there is no need for fear. Your life goes on quite as usual, except for paying more attention to diet and taking care not to get overtired, either at work or play. Women who follow these rules often find themselves feeling better than they did before. The face of a healthy, happy expectant mother acquires a bloom and radiance that more than offset her clumsy torso. See if your friends don't tell you that they have never seen you looking so lovely.

Husbands Have Rights, Too

In recent years, family relationships have undergone a change. It used to be that the husband earned the living and the wife brought up the children, and that was that. Sometimes the only role the father played, in so far as the children could see, was that of the avenger who led the "bad" offspring to the punishment chamber when he came home from work at night.

Now we realize how necessary it is for the father to gain the deep love and respect from his children which can come only from caring for them and playing with them from the very beginning. The sole responsibility of child rearing is too demanding for the average mother; and the children need a father's companionship and guidance as much as they need the security of a home and three meals a day.

That is why today's father is interested in his baby's welfare even during the long months before it is born. He has the right to know how the infant in embryo is developing and that it is getting a good start in life through proper prenatal care. In a number of cities there are classes for prospective fathers where they learn about caring for babies. Besides this, the husband can read up on the subject, can accompany his wife on her visits to the doctor, and can help her carry out the doctor's instructions.

Emotional Side of Pregnancy

Pregnancy often brings about changes in a woman's emotional reactions, and if her husband understands this, he won't worry and will be able to help his wife through any little upsets that occur. A mother-to-be seems to need more love and sympathy during this time—not to be expressed merely by stuffing pillows behind her back when she sits down, but by the obvious pride a man feels in his wife. She wants to know that she is attractive and charming to her husband with or without a slim figure; she wants to feel that he is looking forward very much to their baby; she wants to plan with him for the new baby.

Spare Her All You Can

Although both of you may have been in the habit of meeting each problem together, right now it is better for you, the prospective father, to bear the brunt in order to spare your wife any unnecessary worrying. By no means should she miss out on good times—she needs, and should have, diversion. But until you see just how pregnancy does affect your wife, it would be better not to show that you are worried about your job, or to bring unexpected guests home to dinner. Watch her to see that she doesn't get too tired; help her make her excuses when she wants to leave a party early. Above all, the two of you should have a lot of fun together now, glorying in the remaining period of two-ness while planning happily toward being three.

Tribulations

Now for the trials and tribulations of pregnancy. We must admit it is not entirely a bed of roses, but certainly most of the thorns can be removed. If you are one of the many afflicted with nausea, know that you will almost certainly be through with it around the third month. Naturally, you will consult your doctor about this, but one very helpful hint is to have a box of crackers or some other dry, starchy food at home, and nibble it at the first woozy sign. Perhaps you feel fine when you wake up, but as soon as you get up, the nausea hits hard. Put some crackers beside your bed the night before, and as soon as you open your eyes in the morning, eat a cracker or two. Something solid in the stomach helps keep nausea away. (All your troubles may be because you believed the opposite to be true.)

Consult your doctor in case of vomiting; certain nutrients are essential for the baby's development early in prenatal life.

Disposition Unpredictable?

Perhaps your special tribulation in the early months is your disposition, particularly if your stomach is acting up. You may be sensitive, easily upset, whereas you have always prided yourself upon being sane and reasonable. Pregnancy does affect some women this way, and it is nothing to worry about. Tremendous changes are taking place in your glandular system—in fact, your entire body is working twice as hard as it usually does—and sometimes, just as in adolescence, this brings about moods and depression. But as your body adjusts to the new state, these disappear.

No Need to Worry about Baby

Obstetricians tell us that many mothers and fathers worry as to whether or not their baby may turn out to be malformed. The cheering word there is that infants who are abnormal in any way are a rarity, and that when a germ plasm is defective, Nature in most instances mercifully does not allow the fetus to come to full term. Much is now known about preventing malformation in utero; also, modern medicine can correct many abnormalities.

Finally, your doctor will probably tell you to notify him immediately if anything unusual occurs.

You should let him know if nausea persists beyond the third month. (Usually it vanishes then, quite magically.) If you have a fall, call him at once, and then lie down until he comes, even though you feel perfectly all right. Notify him if you develop an infection, or have fever, or feel dizzy and faint. Even if you have an appointment with him within a few days, call him if your face or hands get puffy or swollen, and if there is any bleeding or loss of water from the vagina.

Swollen feet, on the other hand, are a usual development as pregnancy progresses. Nevertheless, tell the doctor if they occur.

What to Do about Constipation

Sometimes there is a tendency to be constipated, especially in the later months of pregnancy. Do not take any laxatives or enemas unless these are prescribed by your doctor. You can, however, eat more of the laxative foods such as cereals and breads made of whole grains, leafy vegetables and salads, prunes and figs. And drink several glasses of fruit juice a day. If these measures do not bring relief, ask your doctor for further suggestions.

As Pregnancy Advances

As your breasts grow larger and heavier, you should wear a good supporting bra at all times; some women want to wear one even at night when they are in bed. A well-fitting bra will make you more comfortable and will help your bust line remain firm and attractive. You might prefer to buy one or two nursing bras now. Your breasts may be secreting a substance called "colostrum" which stains clothing, and the nursing bras have compartments for gauze shields.

You will want to keep breasts and nipples scrupulously clean, and this can be done in such a way as to help prepare the nipples for nursing. It might be said here that medical authorities disagree as to the efficacy of these measures, but all feel that they do no harm. If your nipples are either tender or tough, or if one or both are inverted, it is worth trying to do what you can to correct these conditions before the baby is born.

Care of Breasts and Nipples

Before touching your breasts or nipples, be sure your hands are well scrubbed, so that there will be no possibility of infection. With your right hand grasp the dark ring surrounding your right nipple, so that the nipple protrudes. With your left hand, using a rough, clean washcloth and soap and water, wash the breast and nipple with a rotary motion. Then, holding your left breast in like manner with your left hand, wash it in the same way. Rinse with clear water and dry with a rough towel. Some doctors advise that water only, without soap, should be used to wash the nipples. In view of the differences of opinion among doctors as to care of the nipples, your own doctor should advise you after inspecting yours. If there is a tendency toward inversion, he may suggest that two or three times a day you draw out the nipple several times with your fingers. He may also suggest anointing the nipples after washing with a lubricant such as cold cream, lanolin, petroleum jelly, mineral oil, or cocoa butter.

No High Heels, Please

If your feet swell, get larger shoes for the prenatal time. Very high spike heels are undesirable in several ways—they tend to tip you forward and do not offer the secure footing you need. You needn't wear flats entirely, though, if you don't like them. A moderate heel with a broad base should be safe.

Never wear circular garters or roll and twist your hose to hold them up. These can cause a lot of trouble by cutting off the circulation. Support your stockings with a maternity garter belt. You won't need to wear stockings, of course, with maternity slacks or shorts.

As for dresses, the maternity shops offer a wide choice. It is possible to get by with only one dress-up costume—after all, the time is short that you will be restricted to this—but it is nice to have several inexpensive ones for home wear. You can continue to use these for house dresses after the baby comes. When your figure is ungainly, it is a special comfort to be able to look fresh and crisp for your husband and visiting friends.

If backaches and constant weariness should come in the later stages of pregnancy, ask your doctor about a maternity corset—he can tell you where to get the make that he thinks will be most helpful. The right kind of maternity corset supports your back without bringing pressure anywhere. Prenatal exercises are very effective in relieving backache, promoting correct posture, and preparing the body for childbirth. Your doctor may suggest that you attend classes where these exercises are taught. His permission is required.

CHAPTER TWO

Furnishings for the newcomer

Although everything should be ready for Baby's arrival at least a month before the delivery date the doctor has given you—babies have been known to arrive ahead of time, with nary a stitch ready!—we advise you not to go on a mad shopping or sewing spree as soon as you discover you are pregnant. Friends and relatives will give you an amazing amount of things, and you don't want to be overloaded with more than you can ever use.

To be on the safe side, however, it is a good idea to provide the following, which will fill all your baby's real needs in the early months.

A Basic Layette

1. At least three dozen diapers, four if you can afford it. The number will depend upon whether or not you plan to patronize a diaper service (in which case they are furnished), but you should have at least a dozen for emergencies. Diapers may be used for sheets if the baby sleeps in a bassinet.
2. Four to six cotton shirts (long or short sleeves, depending on the climate and time of year when your baby will be born).
3. Four to six nightgowns or kimonos.
4. Four to six receiving blankets.
5. One warm and two lightweight crib-size blankets. (It's good to have more, but remember that these are favorite gifts.)

6. Bassinet or cradle or crib.
7. Two waterproof pads, to fit full size of mattress.
8. Three small waterproof pads.
9. Four to six quilted pads.
10. Three or four crib sheets. (No top sheet is needed.)
11. Two sweaters or sacques.
12. Outdoor clothing, such as a bunting or coat and bonnet.
13. Two waterproof pants, for temporary use.

Undoubtedly there will be added to the above list contributions of sweater sets, lovely little dresses, charmingly embroidered kimonos, and bootees by the score. If someone asks you what you need, don't hesitate to answer frankly. There is less chance of duplication that way, and people do like their gifts to be useful.

When buying your layette, remember how fast babies grow. Instead of the smallest size shirts, for instance, most mothers get size 1 and turn the sleeves up till baby grows into them.

For Baby's Care

For the baby's personal care, you will need:

1. A box of sterile cotton. (The balls are convenient to use.)
2. A small box of sterile gauze squares.
3. A bottle of rubbing alcohol, for care of the baby's navel.
4. Petroleum jelly or the ointment your doctor prescribes for care of a circumcision.
5. Baby cream, oil, lotion, powder.
6. Mild soap or soapless baby cleanser; baby shampoo.
7. Several soft washcloths.
8. Several soft towels, bath-size and small-size.
9. Safety pins.
10. Brush and comb.
11. Rectal thermometer.
12. Diaper pail. (With diaper service, this is usually furnished.)
13. Baby bath with padded dressing table top, or a plastic or enamel baby bathtub and a dressing table.
14. Toiletries tray or basket, for baby's bath and diaper changes.

For the bottle-fed baby you will need eight to ten eight-ounce bottles with nipples and caps; two four-ounce size for water and juice; a bottle brush; a sterilizer or large pot with tight-fitting lid; a few extra nipples. In the variety of nipples and bottles available, there are plastic and disposable nursers.

For the breast-fed baby you will need two or three four-ounce bottles with nipples and caps, for water and juice.

When your doctor starts the baby on solid foods you'll find that a small-bowled, long-handled baby spoon is a help.

Furnishings

If Baby has a room of his own, it should be one that heats well in cold weather and does not get overly warm in hot weather. There should be good ventilation without drafts. During the first weeks, the baby should be in an even temperature of about 70 degrees, day and night. When he is a little older, his room temperature for sleeping can go down to 60 degrees. The room for bathing should be 75 degrees.

If the baby sleeps in your bedroom, his bed can be moved to a warmer room during the night if necessary.

This is what is needed in Baby's room or special corner:

1. A crib, portable bed, bassinet or cradle. A padded clothes basket will do for a while, if placed on a firm stand or table. The main essential for any bed the baby uses is a firm, flat mattress that fits snugly on all sides. Never use a pillow as a mattress or use one under Baby's head. He must sleep on a flat surface so he can easily turn his head from side to side. To protect the mattress from stains and odors, fully cover it with a waterproof pad. Never use thin plastic as waterproofing. Pillow slips or diapers may be used as sheets for a small mattress.

   A bassinet or portable bed with closed sides should not be used too long. As soon as the baby begins to be active he needs more space for exercise. He also needs the chance to look around at his surroundings. By about a month of age he'll enjoy a mobile or bright toys hung over his crib.

2. A chest of drawers which will hold the baby's personal items, including bed linens. The bath tray and medications can stand on the top. Having all the baby's things centralized is a big step saver.

Add to these essential items as you like from the complete list at the end of this chapter.

A Plan for Bathing

You will also make some plan for bathing the baby. A baby bath is a great help, since it not only provides a tub but also a movable top, wonderfully convenient for dressing and undressing the baby. It also provides storage space for oil, swabs, soap and other items for the bath. Lacking a regulation baby bath, an enamel baby tub does quite well. Many mothers use the kitchen sink, first scouring it well. An ordinary wash pan is all you need to use for the sponge baths of the first few weeks.

Most people like to have a baby carriage in the house from the first. Besides its intended function, it can be used for naps indoors and out, for sun baths, and even in place of a bassinet. Moreover, it is unsurpassed for carrying groceries.

Pick Your Hospital

You should decide about the hospital to which you will go several months beforehand, and get your name on the list. Latecomers sometimes have a frantic time finding accommodations. Find out which hospital or hospitals your doctor favors, since in the larger cities, especially, a doctor sends his patients only to certain ones. Then go to see the one you agree on, and decide what type of service you want. These days the stay in the hospital is often limited to four or five days. A private room allows you to get more rest and quiet, and visiting hours are sometimes less restricted. A two-bed room gives you semiprivacy and someone to talk to. A larger ward is the least expensive, and many women prefer the rather festive, sociable atmosphere.

The latest thing in hospital arrangements is the rooming-in plan, in which several mothers share a ward, together with their babies, or each mother is alone with her baby. If there is a hospital in your community with this setup, and you are interested in it, apply at a very early date, for the plan has proved extremely popular, and the number that can be taken at one time is usually very small.

Advantages of Rooming In

This arrangement has many advantages. The mother and baby are together from the first and get used to each other. The mother can feed the baby, change his diapers, and cuddle him, thus being an old hand at mothering when she gets home. The father has a chance to become acquainted with his child, instead of going through the frustrating experience of viewing him only through a glass window. The plan has been found a help toward successful breast feeding. If the mother wishes a little rest, the baby is wheeled into a nearby cubicle, so that his care need not be burdensome.

It is smart to have your bag packed several weeks before the date the doctor has given you for the baby's arrival. The baby may decide to come sooner! And in any event, at the last minute you will probably be too excited to remember every item. You will want:

1. Comb.
2. Brush.
3. Toothbrush.
4. Tooth paste.
5. Soap.
6. Bobby pins.
7. Mirror.
8. Cosmetics.
9. Perhaps a ribbon for your hair.
10. Pen and stationery.
11. Stamps.
12. Bedroom slippers and robe
13. Girdle (prepregnancy size).
14. Sanitary belt and a napkin or two.
15. The garments the baby is to wear home.
16. Timepiece.

The hospital will furnish hospital gowns, but after the first day or so you will probably want something daintier. Two or three pretty pajama tops come in handy, or several short nightgowns. These get soiled or crumpled after a day, so arrange to have enough bed jackets and nightgowns to last your entire stay, or else ask a friend or relative to wash and iron them for you. If you are to be in a private room, you might like a small radio.

Delivery at Home

So many people take it for granted that a woman goes to the hospital to have a baby that home deliveries are almost completely ignored these days. Nevertheless, you may have been secretly thinking about having your baby born at home. If you will not be able to have competent help in your home for a week or two, dismiss the thought instantly. But if you can have the services of a nurse (or should your helper be untrained, a nurse or a doctor should be readily available in case of an emergency), and if you will rigidly follow all orders about taking it easy, there is no reason why you can't do this. The big advantage, of course, is that you can follow the rooming-in plan, your baby being with you from the very first. Your husband, too, will be able to spend much more time with you and the baby.

Your Doctor Must Decide

Before you make this decision, you must talk it over with the doctor and his should be the final word. There may be something about your case that he feels could be handled better in a hospital. He may not feel your home is properly equipped for the delivery of a baby. He may feel that you are the kind of housekeeper who will find it impossible to stay in bed and keep out of the kitchen as long as necessary. (It is quite a temptation, you know, when you are used to running your own home, to jump out of bed and redo some little thing to your own satisfaction, when the way your helper did it would really be quite all right.) Aside from the fact that hospitals have an experienced staff and are equipped to deal with every sort of complication, many women like to be delivered there just because of the rest and freedom from responsibility.

If you and the doctor agree that a home delivery is the thing for you, ask him what preparations you must make—different doctors have their own ideas about this—and get everything ready well ahead of time. Then, to make sure, have the doctor come to your home for an inspection, to see if you have forgotten anything, and to make suggestions.

Layette and Nursery Needs

For your convenience, here is a check list of baby things. Use it as a handy guide. Friends and relatives often ask what a baby needs most to round out its layette. New items are constantly coming on the market. While you may not really need all of them, many will lighten your task as a mother, or add to your baby's well-being.

CLOTHING

- Diapers—3-4 dozen if home laundered; 1 dozen to supplement diaper service
- Diaper pins
- Waterproof pants—2
- Shirts—4-6
- Nightgowns, kimonos, wrappers or sleepers—4-6
- Receiving blankets—4-6
- Sacques or sweaters—2
- Booties or socks and soft shoes
- Dress and slip
- Bunting or pram suit or coat and bonnet
- Creepers or overalls—4
- Rompers or sunsuits—4

FURNISHINGS

- Crib; or portable bed, bassinet or cradle
- Chest of drawers, shelves or other storage unit
- Baby bath; or tub and dressing table or rolling cart
- Reclining infant seat
- Playpen and pad

BEDDING

- Waterproof mattress
- Waterproof pads—2 crib size; 3 small size
- Quilted pads—4-6 small
- Crib sheets—3-4
- Crib blankets—1 warm; 2 lightweight
- Crib bumpers

FEEDING EQUIPMENT

- Bottles, nipples, caps:
  - 8 oz.—8-10 for bottle-fed baby; 2-4 for breast-fed baby
  - 4 oz.—2 for water and juice
- Extra nipples
- Bottle and nipple brush
- Sterilizer
- Bottle warmer
- Feeding dish
- Feeding table-seat or highchair
- Bibs—4
- Feeding spoons—1 long-handled; 1 short-handled

BATH AND TOILET ARTICLES

Bath towels—3-4
Washcloths—2-4
Baby cream, oil, lotion
Baby powder
Sterile cotton, balls, swabs
Brush and comb
Mild soap or a soapless baby cleanser
Baby shampoo
Toiletries tray or basket
Diaper pail
Toilet chair or seat

OUTING EQUIPMENT

Baby carriage
Carriage robe
Portable baby carrier; sling or pack-type baby carrier
Stroller
Car bed; car seat
Strap; harness; seat belt
Diaper bag

SPECIALS FOR MOTHER

Rocking chair
Baby record book
Baby scales
Nursery spray
Night light
Room thermometer
Bath thermometer
Bath apron

CHAPTER THREE

Making childbirth easier

For a week or more before the baby's birth, you may occasionally have pains which soon go away. But if there is a pinkish discharge from the vagina (this is called "the show"), the pains are true labor pains and you should phone the doctor at once. You should also phone him if the bag of water breaks, or if pains stay with you and occur at regular intervals. Your doctor will tell you when to start for the hospital.

At the hospital, you will be taken to a room where you undress, have the pubic hair shaved, are given an enema, and examined rectally. The intern or nurse is feeling, through the wall of your rectum, the dilation stage of your cervix, which is the mouth of the uterus. This has to be fully dilated by the pressure of the baby before the child can be born.

Are You Having "Natural Childbirth"?

Perhaps you and your doctor are following the Read system of "natural childbirth." In this method, the prospective mother goes to school, so to speak. At every visit to the doctor she not only undergoes a physical checkup, but is instructed in the changes taking place in her body. She learns how to do exercises that will relax and strengthen the various muscles used in childbirth. She is carefully informed about each of the three stages of labor—exactly what goes on within her and what she can do to help the process along. In order to make sure that she thoroughly understands the part she must play, she is quizzed on her knowledge. When we understand perfectly what is happening to us and know how we can control it, we lose our fear of the birth process. Doctors have discovered that ignorance and fright are directly responsible for much of the pain experienced at this time. (For further information see Bibliography, page 235.)

Don't Fight the Pains

In any event, you can do a lot yourself to make things easier. *Do not tense up and fight the pain.* This actually makes the pain worse and lengthens the time of labor—the fear-tension-pain reaction mentioned by Dr. Read. It may be difficult at first, but try your best to relax during the contractions and to breathe regularly. Very soon, you will see that even though you are experiencing pain, it is not unbearable; some women find that the pain disappears entirely when they relax. If you take it easy during labor and rest while you can, you will save your strength for the time when you need it. If your husband is allowed to be with you at this time, ask him to read aloud, from one of the books on natural childbirth, those paragraphs which pertain to your current stage of labor, even though you have not hitherto followed the Read method. Mothers report that just this much has been a help.

About Anesthetics

There are many different types of anesthesia, and your doctor will know what is best for you. For instance, you may have read of caudal anesthesia and think it would be very nice to have it. But your doctor probably knows that, excellent as it is when properly used, caudal anesthesia in inexpert hands can be dangerous. Unless your hospital or community boasts a technician in whom your doctor has all confidence, it would be unwise for you to insist on this technique.

However, an increasing number of women are able to do with very little anesthetic or none at all, by relaxing, concentrating on having the baby, and not being frightened. In fact, the attitude today has changed from, "Oh my dear, I had the most ghastly time, you have no idea how awful it was," to "Oh, it was wonderful. I didn't have any drugs at all, and the whole thing was so interesting."

There has been so much written lately about natural, drugless deliveries that the woman who really does need an anesthetic has been put on the defensive. She doesn't want people to think she is the whining, complaining type who "refuses to take it," when she knows this isn't the case. Even Dr. Read always had an anesthetic ready in case his patient required it. So let's hasten to say there is no reason at all to be ashamed of yourself if your doctor finds you need the help of one.

In any case, you may be surprised to learn that the hard, pushing pains, when they come, are a great relief. At last you are doing something to help the baby along, and physically it feels good to push. Once these start, the birth of your baby is right around the corner. You will be wheeled into the delivery room, and pretty soon your son or daughter is there to be seen and held. Your tummy is beautifully flat; you are actually able to see your feet.

Differences in Delivery

Usually a baby is born head first, and that is the easiest way, but every so often a baby is turned around, his buttocks presented at the opening of the uterus. This is called "breech presentation." Sometimes the doctor is able to turn the baby around again so that the head is first to arrive and the delivery proceeds normally. Other times, the baby stubbornly insists on having his own way and once more swings his bottom into position. In this case, the doctor reaches inside, gently pulling out first one leg and then the other, then the arms, and finally the head. This shouldn't bother you at all, since the doctor isn't worried and he is doing all the work.

Caesarean Section

If you are slated for a Caesarean section, you will be relieved to learn that it is a common operation that nowadays puts hardly any more strain on the mother than spontaneous delivery. In one respect at least you will be the envy of every other mother in the neighborhood–

you can decide on the day and the hour of your baby's birth! (However, sometimes the doctor waits until labor has started, if you are a border case, in the hope that a Caesarean will prove to be unnecessary after all.) The incision in the lower abdomen and uterus and the removal of the baby take only a few minutes; a much longer time is required to close up the opening, as doctors take very special care to sew up each inner layer of your insides so that you will soon be as good as new. Your convalescence is like any other maternity case—you will be up and walking around within a few days. Just because you have had one Caesarean delivery doesn't mean necessarily that your next baby must be born that way, too. Sometimes a woman's condition changes enough to enable subsequent babies to come normally. Even if a Caesarean section is necessary for each of your babies, you can still have several children, provided your general health is good.

Forceps Delivery

Another word that may strike fear into your heart, simply because you know so little about it, is "forceps." Doctors never use forceps unless they have to, and they are so skilled in the operation of this device that there is rarely any danger to the infant. Occasionally, a baby can't arrive all by himself or else is so long in coming that his life is endangered. Sometimes all the doctor has to do is grasp the head with his fingers and help the baby move forward, but there are times when this isn't enough and forceps are indicated. These are handles crossed in a scissor design, with flat grips on the end shaped to fit comfortably on the baby's head. The doctor knows just where to place these so that with a few gentle pulls the baby is born easily and quickly. Perhaps your baby will have a few red spots on his head where the forceps were, but these will soon disappear.

With or without "differences," more and more mothers today, who followed their doctor's advice throughout pregnancy and who are able to relax for the birth task, are finding that childbirth hasn't been an ordeal at all; it has been an intensely interesting, thrilling experience.

CHAPTER FOUR

Hints for the hospital stay

The baby is born! After an excited chat with your husband about the wonderful fact that you have a baby, you are bundled into bed and told to get a good, long sleep. A word to father is advisable: This is no time to be frank if you see the baby as a grimacing, purplish-red creature with an alarmingly shaped head. A baby's soft, malleable skull may be squeezed into weird proportions during the birth processs. But don't worry about it. It quickly goes back to the contours it was meant to have. So agree with your wife if she tells you the baby is beautiful, and we promise that within a very short time you, too, will honestly believe your baby is the most wonderful, the most intelligent, the loveliest child you have ever seen. It will be a source of constant amazement to you that other people think the same thing about *their* offspring, too.

What Afterpains Are

Although a woman usually isn't bothered by afterpains with her first child, they occur often enough to warrant an explanation here. A few hours after the baby's birth, you may get what seem to be labor pains again. No, it isn't twins, as a rule. Ordinarily it is the uterus contracting, perhaps trying to expel a clot of blood or just trying to get back to its normal size. If the pains are so strong that you have trouble sleeping, the nurse may give you a sedative. The baby won't be brought in to you for several hours, as the two of you need a rest.

A Word about Nurses

For the past few years there has been a great shortage of nurses; rarely are there enough in a hospital to give you extra attention. You should understand that the few nurses on your floor have a tremendous amount of work to do each day, much of which is unpleasant and grueling. They don't wake you up at daybreak just to be mean—they have to get started early in order to take care of every patient. You will find the nurses very sweet and helpful if you don't bother them for extra service and if you are appreciative of what they are able to do for you.

Of course, you should ask for help when you really need it, especially during the time when your baby is learning to nurse at the breast. It is most important that the baby gets off to a good start, and since mother and infant are both new to the process, they can get many good pointers from the hospital personnel.

Reasons for Breast Feeding

We are taking it for granted that you plan to nurse your baby, since it is far and away the best thing for him. The reasons for breast feeding are numerous, touching on all phases of the baby's development.

1. Mother's milk comes conveniently sterilized, heated to the correct temperature, and mixed in the best formula that has yet been devised for the human infant. It supplies all nutriments (except sufficient amounts of vitamins D and C) needed by a young baby, in a form which makes for good digestion—hence, contentment.

2. Authorities believe that the breast-fed baby has an immunity to many diseases, this immunity lasting in a corresponding ratio to the length of time he has been nursed. It is a wonderful thing that you have the power to keep your child from contracting certain illnesses that are dangerous to the small baby.

3. A warm, close relationship grows between mother and baby, so important to his emotional growth. And nursing helps a mother to express in a particularly intimate way the pride and tender-

ness she feels toward her baby. Later, when your husband boasts that you nursed Junior for six or seven or however many months it was, you will feel pretty proud.

4. The breast stimulation caused by the suckling aids greatly in getting the uterus back to normal size and position, thus giving you a good figure much sooner.

Contrary to ideas held by many women, nursing does *not* ruin the shape of the breasts. If your breasts were originally underdeveloped, they will now become fuller; if they were about right to begin with and you have been careful to wear a supporting bra, they will remain about the same—perhaps a little larger, but not sagging.

Sometimes There Are Difficulties

But with even as natural and desirable a thing as nursing a baby there is sometimes trouble and bewilderment for the mother. Perhaps your friends have not been able to nurse their babies, and however much you want to perform this function, you may fear that you, too, will not succeed. A famous obstetrician who has devoted much attention to breast feeding believes that the modern mother's secret fear of failing is one of the big reasons for failure.

The writer's own experience presents a good illustration of this. My first baby was born in an Ohio hospital, with no special conditions to worry me, and the milk came bountifully. My second was born in Central America, where germs and intestinal parasites swarmed, and I felt that I had to breast-feed my baby if she was to survive. It was so much on my mind, and I was so tense and anxious about it, that I couldn't produce a drop!

The nurse shook her head and said there was nothing to be done. Then my doctor came in. "Why of course you will have milk," he assured me. "I am going to give you some pills, and next feeding time you will have lots of milk." Next feeding time I did. Later I learned those were sugar pills—what the medical profession calls a "placebo," something to make you think you are getting medicine when you aren't. What the doctor did was to reassure me and allay my fears, and the milk glands attended to the rest.

But It Can Be Done

It will hearten you to know that wherever special pains have been taken to help mothers in this respect, the very great majority—some hospitals and doctors report as high as 90 per cent—comes through with flying colors. The medical profession admits that some hospital practices that have been current for many years, and the indifference of many doctors to breast feeding, have made it hard for mothers who wanted to nurse their babies.

The two things now considered most harmful to successful breast feeding are bottles given routinely in the nursery—that is, before there is any indication that the baby is going to need a bottle—and insufficient instruction of the new mother in the early phases of nursing.

Get Your Doctor on Your Side

So don't hesitate to ask your doctor to look out for your baby's interests in this matter. Or, if you are planning to have a pediatrician care for the baby, it is quite proper to ask him to take over as soon as the baby is born. It will then be his responsibility to handle things from the nursery standpoint, while the obstetrician looks after your welfare. Either the obstetrician or pediatrician can leave orders that no bottles shall be given unless or until he decides they are necessary. He may also be able to arrange with the obstetrical superintendent to have a nurse stay with you during the first time or two you nurse the baby to help you get started right. Just these two things may mean the difference between successful breast feeding and failure. If still further help is needed, don't hesitate to ask for it!

First Breast-feeding Experience

So now let us imagine that the nurse brings your baby to you for his first table d'hôte meal. This is always a happy occasion—for the nurses seem to take as much pride in a fine infant as do the parents. Have her show you the best position for you to assume—head lifted a little by pillows, the baby fitting snugly into your arm, with the nipple easily available. If the baby is good and hungry, as he should be under a no-bottle-in-the-nursery policy, he may find the nipple for himself. If he doesn't, have the nurse show you how to get it into his mouth, every bit of it, including the brown circle at the base. Baby may look weak and defenseless, but what those vise-like jaws can do to a tender nipple tip as they clamp down on it we wouldn't have happen to *you*! If you have an inverted nipple, in spite of the manipulation you have given it during pregnancy, have the nurse help you to get it out.

Most hungry babies will take the nipple voraciously once they have made contact, but yours may possibly have to be taught to suck. A gentle tickling on his cheek may bring about the desired result. After the baby starts to nurse, hold your breast back from his nostrils so that he will be able to breathe easily.

You don't need to worry about the amount the baby gets in these first efforts. For the first two or three days there is no milk in the breasts anyway, only the clear substance called "colostrum." All babies lose weight until the real milk appears. The hungrier the baby gets, the harder he will try next time he is brought in; and the more relaxed and unworried you are, the easier it will be for the two of you to get together. If you are still having trouble after three or four feeding periods, tell your doctor and ask for further assistance. But the chances are you won't have trouble.

At the end of five minutes—for that's as long as the baby should nurse the first few times—be careful to get the nipple out again, undamaged. The trick is to pry his jaws open gently with your thumb and forefinger, and let the nipple slip out.

Finally, have the nurse give you a lesson in burping the baby. As you probably know, this process gets rid of the gas bubble that often forms in a baby's stomach as he eats and that cannot escape while the infant is in a prone position. So after each feeding, you will lift the baby up over your shoulder and pat his back gently. When feedings are lengthened, whether the baby is breast or bottle fed, it may be a good idea to interrupt the feeding once or twice to do this.

Although the baby nurses for only a few minutes at first, the breast should be emptied so the milk-producing glands will keep on working. It is possible that the milk may appear suddenly, filling the breasts until they are swollen and hard. It is quite natural for the breasts to become painful at this time, and you may run a fever. Some doctors recommend hot packs to stimulate the flow and give relief. Your doctor may advise a breast pump or he may suggest manual expression of the milk between feedings. Sometimes the breasts become "caked" because the baby has been unable to get enough milk. This condition is difficult to relieve with either breast pump or manual expression. Take precautions against it by expressing enough milk from an over-distended breast to allow the baby to nurse properly. Unless his mouth covers the entire areola (the dark area surrounding the nipple) he cannot squeeze the sinuses behind the areola where the milk collects. It is this pressure that forces the milk through the nipple. If he mouths the nipple alone it can become sore or cracked.

It is the custom in many hospitals to offer one breast only per feeding. This is a good idea the first few days, as it gives tender nipples a chance to rest. Later, however, you may find that your baby wants more. Don't hesitate to offer the second breast if he still seems hungry. Just remember that one breast should be completely emptied at each feeding time. If the baby doesn't do this, ask the nurse or doctor to show you how to manually express your milk. Start the baby next time on the second breast, the one from which he nursed least. A small safety pin fastened in your bra will help remind you which breast should be offered first each time.

As the baby learns to nurse strongly and empties the breast, the swelling and pain will disappear. If your nipples are tender, you will find nursing a bit of an ordeal for the first few days, but they will toughen. The doctor may prescribe an ointment for soreness. But the best preventive is making sure the baby takes the proper hold for nursing, as described above. Cover the nipple with a circle of wax paper and some tissues to absorb leakage. Don't try to nurse for too long a period at first. The five-minute intervals should be lengthened gradually—your doctor will advise about this.

One more point. It is the custom in many hospitals to give a bottle in the nursery at 2:00 A.M. in order to allow the mother an unbroken sleep. However, it is nursing that stimulates the production of milk, and your unbroken sleep may be gotten at the expense of dried-up breasts. Ask to have the baby brought in to you at every feeding time.

Milk and Mental State

Your mental state has a direct bearing on your milk; after an emotional upset, milk production slows down or the milk itself may disagree slightly with the baby. Just worrying that you won't have enough milk can cause trouble. So be as calm and as confident as possible.

If you are producing milk, the situation is well in hand, even though the doctor may decide that you aren't producing enough for your baby's needs and order complementary bottles. Many mothers find that these bottles are unnecessary after they get home from the hospital. It often takes six weeks for a milk supply to become firmly established. Previous to that time, it will be quite natural for you to have ups and downs. Don't let these discourage you!

For Those Who Can't Breast-feed

These are the methods by which doctors and hospitals who have interested themselves in breast feeding are helping mothers to nurse their infants. But there are still some women who seem unable to do so—perhaps for deep psychological reasons. Some have a physical condition which makes breast feeding unwise. There are some who, because of a situation or circumstances in their lives, have reason to feel that breast feeding would be a strain and a burden instead of the joy it should be, and there are many who work away from home during the day. If you are in the third-mentioned class, do nurse your baby for as long as you can; even the six weeks that you should take off in order to get back into working condition will make a difference to the baby, and to you, too.

Where breast feeding is impossible for any reason, there are excellent formulas. Your doctor will give you one, suited to your infant's peculiar needs. And if you have made a valiant effort, you need feel no heartbreak. The mother's will to do everything she can for her baby's welfare is one of the important arguments for breast feeding. If you have the will, but are defeated by circumstance from carrying it out, your baby will not feel cheated.

Back to Normal

In recent years, doctors have discovered that the sooner a mother gets out of bed and resumes normal activities, the better she feels. It was the two weeks mothers used to spend in bed, rather than the childbearing, that was weakening. It's true that the first time you sit up in bed you may suddenly decide to lie down again immediately, but most doctors have their patients up and around by the second or third day. (The writer was sent home on the fourth day after her first baby was born.)

Now, before you go home, is a fine time to fill out and send the birth announcements. Here's hoping you and your husband have selected the form of announcement before you went to the hospital. But it is one of life's paradoxes that a woman who would choose a starkly simple announcement marries a husband who likes either the florid or coy type, and vice versa. If the two of you can reach a compromise ahead of time, wedded bliss will progress more smoothly.

If all goes well, here is your chance to catch up a bit on a book or two that your friends have been telling you about, and to write some letters that have gone unanswered during the last dreamy months of pregnancy. But it is even more important now than it was before to take it easy and drop any activity when you begin to tire. Fond as you are of family and friends who come to see you, send them home when the noise and conversation become too much for you. If you are too tenderhearted to do this yourself, you might arrange beforehand with a nurse to ask all guests to leave when you switch on your light. The rule some hospitals have of limiting visitors is excellent.

Give Daddy a Chance

As we said before, one of the big advantages of the rooming-in plan is that Father has a chance to hold and love his baby. But if you weren't lucky enough to get in on this, there is something you should know about men. The father is rare who can fall deeply in love with a newborn baby he has seen only for a minute through a pane of glass. When you are chatting ecstatically about your wonder child, you may notice your husband looking bored, obviously wanting to talk about something else. Don't be hurt; wait until you have the two of them home together. A young man we know explained to his wife that she mustn't expect him to be very fond of the child until it was about five years old and showing some degree of intelligence. Oh, he would be kind to it, but no love, understand? But when the baby came home from the hospital, he carried his new daughter from the car into the house and was heard to say, "Why, you're cute!" Then he called to his wife, "Hey, honey, I think I like her!" You can guess the rest. And when a husband reaches this point, he'll enjoy having you talk about the baby and will do his full share of it.

Do everything you can to cement your husband's affection for his offspring. The baby isn't your exclusive property; its heart belongs to Daddy, too. It is your job to build up a fine companionship between father and child; and to do this, you must let them be together from the first. Show your husband how to hold the baby so its head is supported, but if he forgets once or twice don't snap *his* head off. Baby's head won't snap off either; it is securely fastened on. Also, listen to the father's suggestions, and follow all of them you can. The co-op method in family life is the most beneficial to all concerned, so for Junior's sake, start now.

CHAPTER FIVE

Home at last!

You have been champing at the bit, asking the doctor to please let you take yourself and your baby home, but now that the day is actually here, you may be getting a little stage fright. The baby is such a tiny thing, you've never had a baby before, and what on earth does one *do* with a newborn infant? Everything is quite all right, though. The baby is not nearly so delicate as he seems and he won't break in two if you touch him. Everything in the world is new to him; an inexperienced mother will seem all right to him because he has no one to compare her to.

Make everything as easy for yourself as possible and be confident that things will work out well. If your mother or another relative cannot stay with you, you should have paid help. Whoever it is should plan to be with you for about two weeks or until you are truly able to get along all right by yourself.

These Grandmothers Knew Best

And here's another interesting point about human nature. Mothers have long been warned against letting domineering grandparents interfere with the children. But when the Menninger Clinic at Topeka, Kansas, studied the early reactions of a group of normal mothers, they found that nearly all the mothers wanted Grandma to care for the baby while the mothers themselves did the housework! They felt abused when Grandma replied firmly that *she* would do the housework, and the mother could care for the baby. For this was what the grandmothers said in every case, and they were absolutely right. The help you have, paid or otherwise, *should* attend to the housework while you attend to the baby. If you become exhausted, that is a different matter; then you will want some help with the baby, too. Of course, if your husband is your helper in this strenuous time, as is more and more the case nowadays, it should be share and share alike. Dad is as much entitled as you are to the deep, close bond that comes with meeting Baby's various needs.

Diaper service is a godsend if you can manage to have it. Another energy saver is the disposal diaper, which you could use the first few days that you are on your own. These are not meant for day-in and day-out use but help wonderfully to tide over an emergency.

How "Self-demand" Works

Many doctors nowadays allow the baby to eat whenever he is hungry and to sleep as long or as little as he cares to. This has come to be known as the "self-demand" method; and at first the baby may be very irregular, with feeding periods ranging anywhere from two hours to six hours apart.

There are babies—bless them—who immediately fit into a regular three- or four-hour schedule. If yours does, so much the better. In the average hospital, all babies are fed at four-hour intervals, unless the doctor has ordered a three-hour schedule. If your baby always seems hungry at the scheduled mealtime, nurses eagerly and then is contented, the regular schedule is probably right for him and he will keep on it, with only a few digressions now and then.

But if the baby came to you too sleepy to eat or too upset from exhaustive crying, you will need to make some changes when you get home. Feed him whenever he is hungry. He may need to eat as often as every two hours during the first few days at home in order to get caught up with the nutrition he missed at the hospital. Or he may be tired from crying and want to sleep straight through a feeding. Let him. If he is asleep at feeding time, he needs the sleep more than the food; when his hunger pangs become strong enough, he will awaken and ask to be fed.

Occasionally, the two needs are equally strong at the same time—he cries to be fed, nurses for only five minutes or less, then drops off to sleep. Tickle his cheek or his feet to keep him awake long enough to finish the feeding, but don't insist. If he is just too sleepy, put him back to bed. He may sleep only half an hour and then be ready for a full meal, or maybe the mere appetizer was enough to put him in dreamland for hours. To give you some idea of his varying schedule: He may eat every two and one-half hours for an entire twenty-four hour day, and the next day he may eat every five hours, with an occasional shorter period slipped in. He may eat at 6:00 A.M. and 8:00 A.M., then sleep until 3:00 P.M. No two days may be the same, yet each day may go as regularly as clockwork, according to its own pattern.

It Doesn't Last Forever

Unless you understand that this type of day doesn't continue indefinitely, you have every reason to be skeptical of the self-demand method. Nobody wants a spoiled child who gets everything he wants when he wants it, without regard to the convenience of other people. But that is not the idea of self-demand. Its purpose is to make the baby's adjustment to life easier, to help him thrive and be happy much sooner. It doesn't take long for him to make his adjustments if your supply of breast milk is sufficient (or the formula a good one), and once this pleasant state is arrived at, the baby, with help from you, begins to establish a set pattern. As a matter of fact, babies work naturally into regularity and most of them will attain it easily with a little parental help. (See pages 50–52 for information on managing the change from self-demand to a convenient pattern in baby's daily life.)

When Baby Cries

We are not saying that every time the little fellow cries he is necessarily hungry. There are any number of reasons other than hunger that can make him unhappy. Change his diapers if they are wet. Maybe that was all that was troubling him. Or perhaps he was tired of sleeping in the same position, in which case you can tuck a tightly rolled blanket behind his back to support him more or less on one side. A tiny child cannot turn himself and will appreciate it if you help him move around a bit. Perhaps he was too hot or too cold; add or remove clothing and blankets accordingly. Make sure that the mattress and sheet are smooth and comfortable and that conditions are conducive to sleep. Sometimes a little gas remains in the baby's stomach after the last feeding; try burping him. If it is about halfway between feeding times, offer him lukewarm boiled water. Some babies may be unwilling to drink any water until they are several months old, but always give yours the opportunity.

Reassurance Needed

If the baby continues to cry after you have checked all the above things, hold him, rock him, and talk to him softly. Being out in the world for the first time must be lonely and frightening. Or maybe he was just on the point of going to sleep and wants to be left alone. After a while, you will discover that he has a special way of crying when he is hungry, another to indicate he is uncomfortable, still another when he is tired and sleepy. When you can interpret his cries, life will become much simpler. The important thing about the newer attitudes is that the mother is given freedom to work and experiment with her baby, and thus to find out for herself just what he needs.

The foregoing suggestions apply to nighttime as well as daytime hours. Under self-demand, there is no more setting of the alarm for a 2:00 A.M. feeding. The night feedings come at whatever hour the baby asks for them. Strangely enough, this usually makes for more peaceful nights.

For a hungry baby who must wait until 2:00 A.M. to be fed is going to put in the intervening time telling everyone how much he is being persecuted. When food finally arrives, he may be too worn out to eat very much, and so start crying again at 3:00 A.M. That has happened in many a household. But if you feed him when you hear his first real hunger cries at 1:00 A.M., let us say, he is likely to slumber contentedly until well into the dawn.

There is no escape from some getting up at night while a baby is little and his stomach capacity is small. Until Mother regains her strength, either the helper or Dad should get out of bed as soon as Junior indicates he is serious about something (little snufflings or tentative wails don't count) and either bring the little fellow to Mother for a breast feeding or warm a bottle and administer it. If food doesn't seem to be the answer, go through the list of possible needs that we mentioned just previously. Prompt attention to Junior's cries is the quickest way to let the household settle down to sleep again.

Be cheered by the fact that as a baby begins to plump out from his self-demand daytime meals, he is going to sleep for longer and longer intervals at night. (We have more to say about that in the next chapter.) The time will probably come soon when Mother will feel equal to taking over the night duty, and Dad can catch up on his sleep again. And the well-fed, comfortable baby doesn't demand middle-of-the-night attention for very many weeks. If your baby should continue night after night to wail and refuse to be comforted, by all means let your doctor know. Perhaps your supply of milk is not sufficient or the formula needs strengthening. Where all is well in the new baby's world, he may disturb his parents' rest once or twice during the night but that is all. Wholly sleepless nights are a definite sign that something is wrong.

Do attend to your baby's wants other than eating and sleeping with as much regularity as you can. Give him his bath at the same time each day—midmorning is usual, but any convenient time is all right. Give him his airing at the same time. Don't wake him up for his bath or feeding or airing, we hasten to say, but carry out your program as near to the appointed hour as the baby permits. That is the beginning step toward reasonable regularity in all things.

Mothers' Fears

Not long ago, a group of eminent obstetricians, pediatricians, and psychiatrists got together and discussed the reactions to motherhood of normal, well-balanced women, as they had observed them. They agreed that certain fears were characteristic in the first days at home with a new baby.

One common fear is that the baby will stop breathing. This is due to the fact that new babies breathe quite shallowly. You may find yourself wanting to steal in frequently and hang over the crib, reassuring yourself that respiration is still going on. There is nothing wrong with that, but if your baby was pronounced healthy by the doctor, you have no cause for worry. When your baby gets safely into the world, every cell in his body is organized to keep him there.

The Facts about Smothering

A second common fear is that the baby will smother. You may not know of a case firsthand, but you have read about them. It may be so much on your mind that you worry about putting the baby on his stomach to sleep—often a favorite position, and one in which there is little chance of choking if the baby should vomit.

The fact is, according to medical authorities, infant deaths attributed to suffocation are in almost all cases due to a sudden, overwhelming infection. Autopsies have proved this in innumerable cases. The symptoms of infection may have been too slight to be noticed. In many cases, infant deaths have been recorded as caused by suffocation when no autopsy, or an incomplete one, has been performed.

One danger which all mothers should know about is thin plastic, the type that is often used to cover clothes after dry-cleaning. This can adhere to a baby's or young child's face, shutting off air and causing him to suffocate. That is why we cautioned you in Chapter Two not to use thin plastic as waterproofing for the baby's mattress. Bags of this material are often used in packaging; they should be removed and destroyed as soon as the article is in your home, so there is no chance that a young child will get hold of them to play with.

It's best not to leave extra blankets in the bed. Keep the newborn's room temperature at 70 degrees and many covers won't be needed. See that all blankets are securely anchored under the mattress. Have no loose ties or strings that can get wrapped about the baby's throat. Don't hesitate to go to him and investigate if he cries. With a careful, attentive mother close by, there is practically no chance that your baby will either smother or strangle himself.

If You Think Baby Is Ill

It is natural for new parents to imagine something very serious if the baby shows signs of illness, or if they just think he is ill. Don't waste time worrying—phone the doctor and describe the condition to him. He will do whatever is necessary. Things to tell the doctor about are:

1. A cold.
2. Fever—rectal temperature of 101 degrees or above. (The way to take the baby's temperature is described on page 221.)
3. Vomiting.
4. Refusal to eat for more than a day's time.
5. Continual crying or wailing as though he were in pain.
6. Failure to gain over a period of a week or two.
7. Sudden change in bowel movements or urine.
8. Any other condition that worries you. (See sections on pages 220 and 221-224—When Baby Is Sick and Nursing Techniques.)

Doctors are used to the alarms of early parenthood and don't mind being called even when these are false alarms. Put your baby's health welfare in your doctor's capable hands and have no fears on this score. The fact is that the baby who comes through his first week of life with flying colors has announced his firm intention of staying on in this interesting world. Nature has given tiny babies an immunity to a number of diseases that could be serious for them (though this isn't invariable, and you will shield your baby from infections just the same). Medical science offers almost miraculous cures today for nearly all the ailments a baby can incur. If you let your doctor know as soon as illness signs appear, there is scarcely any condition that he won't be able to cope with successfully.

Giving the Bath

Another stressful time for the new mother is the giving of the first baths. We knew a trained nurse who had bathed many brand-new babies. Nevertheless, when it came to bathing her own for the first time, she confessed to as much stage fright as if she had never handled a baby before!

Some doctors are now doing away with baths for the first six weeks or so. The baby is cleaned with oil in the diaper region, and that is all. But your doctor may not be of this persuasion. And after the first bath or two, you will find that this is no fearsome process but one both you and the baby will look forward to.

The house is usually warm and your most pressing chores are out of the way by 9:30 or so in the morning, so this is a good time to give the daily bath. Also, the baby appreciates the freshening up after having lain much of the night in wet diapers.

Sponge Baths First

Until his navel is healed, you will give a sponge bath. If you are still weak and shaky, you can do this sitting down and holding the baby in your lap.

Use a low chair, and place a low table nearby. Lay out on the table everything you will need. This will include mild soap, small washcloth, and big, soft bath towel, lots of sterile cotton wads (you can buy these in a size easy to use, or pull a number from a roll of sterile cotton, shaping them into balls with your fingers); oil, fresh clothing for Baby. Loosen the lids of the oil- and boric-solution bottles. Lay a newspaper open by your chair to catch soiled clothing and used swabs.

The last thing before you pick up the baby, fill a basin with lukewarm water and add this to your equipment, plus a pitcher of hot water in case the water in the basin gets too cold before you have finished.

Now pick up the baby, stripping his bed covers back as you do so. Sit in the chair, spreading your knees to make a good lap.

Remove the soiled clothing and drop it on the newspaper. Place a clean diaper underneath the baby and cover him with a large, soft bath towel.

Moisten a cotton wad in the boric acid water and with one wipe clean off any mucus around his eyes. Use each wad once and discard it. Always use a fresh wad for each eye. (Many babies have runny eyes during the first few weeks and it is usually nothing to worry about. However, tell your doctor about it.)

If there is any dirt in his nose, twist a moistened piece of cotton into a point and work the dirt out. Never use anything hard or stiff—just the twist of cotton. Only the outside of his ears should be washed. Never put anything into the inner ear.

Next, sponge off his face with clear water, using the washcloth, and gently pat it dry. Now wash an arm with soap, rinse, dry, and cover it with the towel while you attend to the other arm. Wash his neck, chest, and tummy and lay the towel over his upper body. Wash each leg, covering it afterward; then the genitals.

In the case of a boy, wash the penis as you would any other part of the body. Doctors no longer advise that the foreskin of an uncircumcised male be pulled back—an anxious operation for the mother, and often a painful one for the baby. But if your baby has been circumcised and the penis is not yet healed, put a dab of petroleum jelly on a small piece of gauze and wrap it around the end of the penis. Keep the penis covered this way until healed.

With a girl, separate the outer lips of the vulva with one hand and run several moistened wads of cotton across it until it is clean. Always clean a little girl with a front-to-back motion, as fecal matter from the anus can start an infection in the vagina.

Now flop the baby over on his tummy and sponge off his back, drying always with a patting rather than a rubbing motion.

With the front side uppermost again, oil the scalp and all creases, including the one behind the ear (but never put oil in ears, eyes, or nose), using a different wad of cotton for each crease. Finish off, if you like, with a dusting of powder. Diaper him, then put on his shirt. Finish the dressing, and snuggle him for a few minutes while congratulating yourself upon how smoothly it all went. Finally, lay the baby on a big bed or couch to exercise while you make his bed afresh, so that he can rest for a few minutes before feeding time.

Twice a week his scalp should be washed, first with a soapy washcloth, then with one from which the soap has been rinsed out.

Caring for the Navel

If you come home from the hospital on the fourth or fifth day, a bit of the cord may still be attached to the baby's navel. It will drop off before long and leave a little sore. Cleanse this with alcohol at each bath time as long as there is any oozing, and cover it with one of your sterile gauze pads. If this gets wet from the baby's diaper, apply a fresh pad when you change the baby. Even after the navel is completely healed, it may stick out a little. This merely means that the abdominal muscles have not yet grown together. Should the navel or surrounding area become red, notify your doctor at once, for this indicates infection.

In some babies, the breasts swell up a few days after birth. There actually is milk in them! This happens as often in boy babies as in girls. All it means is that some of the hormones in your body that help you make milk have spilled over into the baby's circulation just before birth. Leave the breasts alone if they swell. They will subside in a few days.

Small red areas over a baby's eyes, or between the eyes, or at the back of the neck are seen frequently. These, too, will fade away in a few weeks' time.

Now for the Tub Bath

As soon as you feel strong enough, the sponge bath can be given in the baby bath or on a table that has been well padded. Don't leave the little fellow for a moment, though; for, tiny as he is, he might wriggle off.

When the navel is healed, he is ready for a tub bath. Fill the baby bath, or basin, with three or four inches of lukewarm water. Wash his head in the sponge-bath method, then quickly soap all the rest of him and lower him into the tub, holding his buttocks in your left hand, his head supported by your arm. If you lay a hand towel on the bottom of the tub, he won't slip. If you haven't a baby bath providing a support for his head, slide your hand up from his buttocks and use it to support his head above the water. Rinse him off with the washcloth. Although he shouldn't stay in the water for more than a very few minutes, he usually enjoys an extra moment of having the water gently splashed over his body. Now remove him and envelop him immediately in a towel. Pat him thoroughly dry, apply lotion, oil or powder, and dress him.

Diaper Care

Use common sense in changing your baby's diapers. They don't need to be changed every time he wets—at that rate you'd never get anything else done all day. And never wake him to clean him up. Of course you will change him when he is uncomfortable, and whenever you get him up.

Have a covered pail handy, containing water with a deodorizing, softening agent for diapers, into which you drop the wet diapers. A diaper containing bowel movement is held and rinsed in the flushing toilet, then wrung out before it goes into the pail. At washtime, wring out. Place the diapers in a tub or washing machine and wash in mild suds. Rinse two or three times or until water is clear. If your baby has very delicate skin, you may have to rinse them more times. Hang the diapers in the sun to dry whenever possible. Diapers don't need to be ironed. You will save yourself time and trouble if you fold them into the correct shape for Baby to wear as soon as they are dry.

Don't Neglect Diaper Rash

If your baby develops a diaper rash, call it to your doctor's attention, and also change Baby more often. Diapers and wet bedding should be given special washing and rinsing. Use one of the antiseptic diaper products on the market or a solution recommended by your doctor. He may also prescribe an ointment that will help cure the condition.

Diapers are made of various types of material such as gauze, bird's-eye, cotton knit, and flannelette. Regulation sizes come in squares or rectangles. There are also some on the market that are shaped to fit the baby. To fold the rectangular type of diaper, many mothers find it most convenient to double the diaper twice, lay the baby on it, and fold the excess length as extra protection. For a boy, have the folded-over portion in front; for a girl, place it in back. When the baby is sleeping on his stomach the folded-over part is best in front for both sexes. You might like to experiment with other types of folds as well, such as the one that resembles a kite. To do this, fold the square diagonally to make a triangle. Place Baby in the center of the triangle, with the folded edge about an inch above his waist. Bring three corners together in front, with center one on top, and pin.

Bowel Movements

Each baby has his own schedule for moving his bowels. The breast-fed baby as a rule has more movements per day than the bottle baby. Nursing seems to stimulate the bowels, and often the baby has to stop eating temporarily in order to relieve himself. The movement is extremely soft, yellowish, and with a sweetish odor. If the odor is bad and the color green, he may have a digestive disturbance and you should phone the doctor. The new mother is inclined to be terror-stricken when the baby screams and the movement spurts out quite audibly, but usually this means that the baby's organs are getting used to ordinary digestive duties. A phone call to the doctor will reassure you. Sometimes the baby goes for a long time, two days or more, without producing a single stool. This may be quite normal for him. Always check with your doctor before giving an enema, using a soapstick, or resorting to any other artificial means of producing a movement.

It is usual for the bottle baby to have from one to four movements a day, the number growing less as time goes on. The consistency is ordinarily a little thicker than the stool of a breast-fed child and has a more unpleasant smell, but this varies with the individual baby. As in the breast-fed baby, the thing to watch out for is bad color, marked change in odor, and overmuch liquid and mucus.

Weighing the Baby

You can tell that your child is gaining sufficiently if he is happy, healthy, and eating well. He needn't be weighed except on his regular visits to the doctor's office once a month. If you have baby scales it's best not to weigh him oftener than once a week. Every time you weigh him, be sure it is at the same time of day—before a meal is best—and that he is wearing just a shirt and diaper. At first a baby gains anywhere from 4 to 8 ounces per week. He is growing phenomenally fast right now. Within a few months, though, he begins to slow down, cutting his weight gain to half what it was, by the time he is six months old.

A number of years ago, it was considered that to be healthy and beautiful, a baby had to be fat. Now it is known that just as in adult life, excess weight is not desirable. Babies have different physical builds. Each grows and gains weight at his own normal rate.

How to Make a Formula

If you are bottle feeding, never improvise on the formula, no matter what relatives or friends tell you. If you think the baby needs a change, or an increase in the formula before the doctor orders it, consult him.

Boiling the formula kills dangerous bacteria and also makes it more digestible. One way to sterilize, requiring considerable care, is called the aseptic method: After washing and rinsing, boil or steam the bottles, nipples, caps, and all equipment to be used in preparation of the formula, for five minutes in a covered pot or sterilizer; boil water for the formula five minutes, measure, add sweetening and evaporated milk (washing top of can first), mix well; pour into bottles, insert nipples, cap and refrigerate. If fresh milk is used, boil formula mixture five minutes and strain into bottles.

The following method combines the sterilizing of bottles, nipples, caps, and formula—and so requires less time and care. This method is called terminal sterilization:

Step 1. Assemble your paraphernalia—all you really need, for this method, is a wire bottle rack, a funnel, a tablespoon, a bottle brush, a nipple brush, a quart graduate which has ounces marked on the side, and the ingredients for the formula. And, of course, enough bottles, nipples, and shields for a twenty-four-hour supply.

Step 2. Wash the bottles and nipples, if you have not already done so. (It's a good idea, really, to wash used ones each time you wash dishes, separately of course. Then the biggest part of the job will be done.) With hot soapy water or detergent and the nipple brush, scrub the nipples well, being sure you get all the milk out of the holes. Rinse under the hot-water faucet and set aside. Wash the bottles, scouring every inch of the inside with the bottle brush. Rinse, drain and place in the bottle rack right side up, the ounce markings turned toward you. Drop the bottle caps into the suds.

Step 3. Into the quart graduate, measure out the sweetening called for by the formula, then add the water from the water tap. (If the sweetening is dextro-maltose, and it won't dissolve in the tap water, boil just enough water to dissolve the dextro-maltose, then add enough more from the tap to make your water content.) Next comes the milk. Stir well, pour into the bottles through the funnel, putting as many ounces into each bottle as your baby usually consumes at a meal.

Step 4. Now put the nipples on the bottles. With this method, you don't have to worry about touching the tip, since sterilization is still to come. Rinse the bottle caps under the faucet and place them lightly over the nipples, a little atilt so the steam will be able to reach every part of the nipple. All the foregoing is done while the bottles are in the rack. If you use bottles with nipples that can be pushed down inside the bottle, place the nipples on the bottles with the feeding tip in the inverted position. Screw cap down snugly, then loosen a quarter- or half-turn to allow for steam expansion which might break the bottle.

Step 5. Again from the water tap, fill a bottle, put on nipple and cap, and add to your collection. This is your baby's drinking water for the day.

Step 6. Into a jar which has two lids—one perforated and one solid—put several extra nipples, in case one or more of those on the bottles proves inadequate. Put on the perforated lid, place the jar in the middle of the rack, and drop the solid lid beside it.

Step 7. Pour hot water into the sterilizer to about midpoint of the bottles. Cover tightly and bring to a boil. Let boil for exactly twenty-five minutes. Use a timer if you have one.

Step 8. At the end of twenty-five minutes, turn off the heat, leave lid on and allow bottles to cool slowly. This helps to prevent scum from forming. When cool, screw caps tight and refrigerate.

If scum tends to clog the nipples, insert gauze squares, or strainers made for this purpose, under nipples before sterilizing.

If you use well water, you are advised to have it tested for bacteria and nitrates. If approved for use, boil it for five minutes before putting it in the formula, as an extra precaution. The baby's drinking water, from any source, must be sterilized. Raw milk, even if certified, should not be used in the formula.

Evaporated Milk and Prepared Formulas

Evaporated milk is approximately twice the strength of fresh milk. If you have a fresh-milk formula and must substitute evaporated milk, measure half the milk called for, add an equal amount of water, then add the water specified in the formula.

Prepared formulas are available in both liquid and dry forms requiring only the addition of water before sterilizing. These preparations, as well as the special function formulas (with the exception of lactic acid and protein milks) are not adversely affected by the terminal sterilization method described above. For the liquid ready-to-use brands, sterilize bottles, nipples and caps by boiling or steaming for five minutes, then pour in formula.

How to Give the Bottle

To lessen the chance of swallowed air, hold the baby nearly upright for feeding, and keep the nipple filled with milk. First, warm the bottle in water or a bottle warmer till it is body temperature. Test from time to time by shaking a little onto your wrist. If it brings neither a cold nor a slightly hot sensation, it is exactly right.

After the baby has finished eating, pour out any milk remaining in the bottle, rinse it out, and fill it with cold water. Rinse the nipple well. Set in the bottle rack to await the washing and scrubbing with soapy water.

If any bottles of formula remain after twenty-four hours, do **not use** them for the baby, but make a fresh supply.

As your baby grows both in size and appetite, you will gradually increase the amount of formula. Your doctor will advise you about that. Keep in touch with him and follow his advice about changing the formula in any way.

Freedom Bottle

Once you have established a good supply of milk, your breast-fed baby can have an occasional bottle feeding too, and thus allow you to go to a luncheon or afternoon or evening party when you want to. Ask your doctor for a formula for such a bottle, and prepare it according to the directions we have given for bottle feedings. Thanks to the freedom bottle, the mother who is breast-feeding usually finds that she is no more tied down than her bottle-feeding sisters, and she doesn't have to go through the fuss and bother of fixing a formula every day.

Aside from the good it does you to get out now and then, it is also good for the baby to become accustomed to an occasional bottle. If you should become ill or be forced to take an unexpected trip, a sudden weaning would be much easier for him if he is already familiar with the bottle.

If He Doesn't Like It

You may find that your baby doesn't like milk out of a bottle—he prefers you! There are a few little tricks that help persuade him that good food can come in bottled form. First, try having someone other than yourself give him the bottle. A baby smells breast milk from his mother and is likely to be very annoyed with her for not giving him the breast. When he cannot smell the breast, he is more inclined to accept the bottle. If he still objects, moisten the bottle nipple in a cup of warm, boiled water-and-sugar solution. Making the nipple warm and sweet increases its attractiveness to a baby.

CHAPTER SIX

The first three months

There has been some confusion about the self-demand schedule, and some misgivings on the part of young parents who see their own eating and sleeping and work schedule hopelessly disrupted. Perhaps enough emphasis has not been placed on transferring from self-demand to the more scheduled living necessary for the baby's happiness at later stages. Yet this transition is not hard to make.

The purpose of self-demand, we must remember, is to ease the baby's adjustment to the outside world. A wealth of experience has now shown that babies are happier when their individual needs are taken into account. They cry less—though some crying is always to be expected. They start sleeping through the night at an earlier age. And it is interesting to note that as they become adjusted to the new environment, which is evidenced by contentment most of the time, they begin of their own accord to regularize their hours for eating and sleeping.

Learn to Be Flexible

It is wise, therefore, to adjust your own schedule at first to the baby's irregular—and perhaps seemingly constant—demands. But presently you will observe a regular pattern emerging. With a great many babies, this happens around the third month. But it takes some infants a longer time, others a shorter time. Also, it happens differently with different babies. We do not advise, therefore, that you clamp your baby into a rigid schedule the moment he begins to eat and sleep by a fairly regular pattern. But you can help him to establish this as a habit, and gradually you can help him adjust his schedule to that of the family.

The Night Situation

You would hardly be human if you weren't looking forward to the time when your baby will sleep through the night. Babies, too, like to get a good night's sleep (in spite of that week or so when they experiment with sleeping all day and wanting to be amused all night) and, as we said in the previous chapters, they gradually work toward eliminating their middle-of-the-night meal. Your infant may suddenly decide to sleep from 10:00 P.M. until 6:00 A.M., and that will be that; or he may start taking his 10:00 P.M. feeding later and later until it merges with the one in the middle of the night. In such a case, you are justified in waking him around 10:00 or so to fill him up for the night. Another child delays his 2:00 A.M. feeding a little more each night until it runs into breakfast time. Let him do this in his own way. Never wake him at 2:00 A.M. If he needs this meal, he will be the first to know it. Neither should you try to force the issue of dropping the feeding, as he needs all the milk he wants.

You Can Guide Him

If it looks as if his own pattern, as it emerges, won't be practical for either of you, you can guide him to a more satisfactory arrangement. For instance, if he seems fond of a too early supper, which in turn leads him to want breakfast at the crack of dawn, try playing with him and rocking him for as long as he is happy, thus delaying his supper. Within a few days, you can, in this way, switch him from, let us say, a 4:30 supper to 5:30 or later.

If you have been following our advice about keeping a regular bath time, airing time, and family playtime, when he's awake at the hours for them (you won't wake him up for this), you will find he fits into a schedule much more quickly. Since each day is different and brings new experiences, you mustn't expect that once you do find a schedule you will be able to stick to it like glue. Every schedule must be somewhat elastic. As the baby grows, his needs will change, and the schedule must change with them. Then, too, if your schedule isn't flexible, some unexpected happening (and these occur all the time) will throw you completely off, upsetting everything. You must learn to take things in your stride, fitting in the necessary activities as seems best.

This Gives You the Idea

We suggest a tentative schedule, to give you an idea of how to arrange your own. You will adapt it, of course, to fit your baby's individual needs, and you will alter it when necessary.

6:00 A.M. Change diapers and wet clothing. Nurse or bottle-feed the baby. The average baby takes about twenty minutes to finish. When he is through, take a little time to lie in bed playing quietly with him until you have to get up. By that time he may be ready for another little snooze. Then return him to his bed.

9:30 A.M. Give him his bath. Then place him on a bed or couch where you can keep an eye on him while you remake his bed.

10:00 A.M. Nurse him or give him the bottle.

10:30 A.M. Change him and return him to bed. If the weather is hot, he may sleep better outdoors in his carriage in the shade.

2:00 P.M. Nursing or bottle feeding.

3:00 P.M. Give him an outdoor airing in his carriage. If it is cold outside, keep the tiny baby in the house near an open window, but protected from drafts.

5:00 P.M. Family playtime and cuddling put a happy finish to the day. Let him exercise without any clothes on for a while. There are a few simple exercises you can help the baby to do, giving him a chance to strengthen his muscles. For example, bend his knees back against his abdomen and then stretch them out as straight as they will go. Swing his arms in wide arclike motions—up, above his head, out to the sides, down to the hips. You can adapt many old stand-bys of "setting-up" exercises, but with the baby lying down. Be easy with him, and only attempt exercises that can't possibly be too much for him. His own activities will suggest new exercises as he grows. When he struggles to sit up, hold his hands and help him forward a few inches, then lower him again. But don't force the actual sitting up. Let him accomplish all feats by himself in his own good time; you are just helping him flex the muscles he needs for each step.

6:00 P.M. Nursing or bottle feeding. Get him all dressed for bed, rock him in your arms while you sing to him, and put him to bed. The window should be open, but a temperature of over 65 degress should be maintained in his room for the first few weeks, and 60 degrees after that.

10:00 P.M. Nursing or bottle feeding.

2.00 A.M. Nursing or bottle feeding if he wakes and seems to want it.

That schedule would obviously not do for a baby who is on more of a three-hour plan. If this baby eats at 6:00, 9:00, and 12:00, you would bathe him at 8:30 or 11:30—whichever is more convenient.

Let's Not Be Arbitrary

Remember that none of these times is arbitrary. The baby might wake up for what we call the 10:00 A.M. feeding at 9:00 A.M. or at 11:00 A.M. The same is true of all his activities. Some babies are on a four-hour schedule in the mornings and a three-hour schedule in the afternoons. Do what seems best for your own baby.

Not all men have a 9:00 A.M. to 5:00 P.M. working day. If the man of your house is on a night shift, adapt the baby's schedule to that. A baby can sleep from midnight to noon perfectly well, if it gives him a chance to visit with his father. You just strive for regularity, of course, and see that the baby gets daytime outings, but beyond that you can adjust the daily regime in the most convenient way.

Scheduling Your Work

We have advised you to dismiss all unnecessary housework until you fully regain your strength, but we well know that there are still chores that need to be done. We hope that the person who came to help you stayed long enough to ease you slowly into the household routine, but in these times that is often impossible. You must eat an ample breakfast to carry you through a long day—fruit, whole-grain cereal or toast, eggs, milk. While you are eating, plan your activities for the day as best you can from your knowledge of your baby's schedule.

Sometimes a mother is able to get a little extra time in the early morning if she snuggles the unfed baby into bed with Daddy while she gets the coffee on and breakfast started. This takes Baby's mind off his empty tummy for half an hour while he plays with his father. Then while Daddy is eating, you can settle down, with a glass of juice and a cup of coffee, to nurse Junior.

If he likes to take a nap right after breakfast, you can do a little housecleaning at this time. If you are bathing Baby in the kitchen sink, you will want to get the dishes done, the sink scoured out, and all bath things arranged before you do anything else.

If you are not bathing the baby in the kitchen, it might be a good idea to stack the dishes so that you can wash everything up at once after lunch. Before the baby wakes for his bath, you should be able to make your bed and do either a quick dusting or a diaper wash. If you have a few minutes left, by all means lie down.

Don't forget to drink a glass of liquid from time to time. If you are worried about gaining weight, drink skim milk; it has all the wholesome qualities of whole milk minus the fat.

Time Out for a Rest

After the bath and feeding, lie down again for at least ten minutes. Try propping your feet up on pillows so that they are higher than your head. The blood runs from your feet down to your head, and the effect is very refreshing.

You may be able to do a bit of ironing before lunch. For the next few months, or as long as you nurse your baby, iron only the things that you have to. Smooth and put away without ironing sheets, towels, Baby's kimonos. Wear an apron or smock to save your own dresses. Wear plastic aprons which you can simply wipe off when they are soiled. Many husbands these days have learned to iron a very decent shirt and other things. Perhaps yours could relieve you of this chore for a couple of weeks. If he hasn't this skill, he might help wash diapers, say three nights a week or so, or do the dinner dishes.

Eat a wholesome, simple lunch, wash the morning's collection of dishes, and then snatch another few minutes of rest. After you have fed and bedded the baby, prepare as much of your dinner as you can. Scrub potatoes, fix vegetables, make a casserole, perhaps a simple dessert.

Whenever you have any cooking that involves more than opening a can or defrosting a package, cook double the recipe, then put the unused half away in the refrigerator to bring out again in a day or two. Meat loaf, for example, can be sliced cold, or sliced and fried, or added to a can of tomato soup and poured over rice. Make a double amount of cream sauce when you have a creamed vegetable, and next day use the remainder as a base for creamed soup. Many things can be done with leftover potatoes and other vegetables. A large piece of boiled beef can be eaten "as is" the first night, then cut up for hash the next night. The broth can be made into soup or cooked with noodles. A big batch of chili can be stretched to make a macaroni or rice dish a day or so later.

Use ready mixes as often as you can. The mixes nowadays are very good, and less expensive in many cases than homemade efforts.

Now a Change of Scene

These tasks performed, a change of scene will do more for you now than another nap. Since it is the baby's airing time anyway, you can wheel him to the grocery store while you do your shopping, or take him visiting. This will provide your outdoor exercise, too. When shopping with the baby, never leave the carriage alone outside the store. Wheel it inside where you can watch it; otherwise the carriage might roll into the street, or children with coughs or contagious diseases might play with the baby.

Upon your return home, place the already prepared dinner casserole in the oven, or start the potatoes cooking, then play with and exercise the baby as indicated in the schedule on page 52. However, if your husband's hours permit it, turn over to him these end-of-the-day procedures for the baby. Most fathers are glad to have this opportunity, and can handle them beautifully, given a little practice.

Maybe Dad Will Help

Make an effort to do the dishes immediately after dinner (you are justified in using paper plates for the first few days). If you once sit down before the dishes are done, your mind keeps returning to them, magnifying the job until it seems as if a whole week's work is waiting for you in the kitchen sink. Today's husband is usually perfectly willing to help with the dishes.

You probably will find the weekly house cleaning too much of an undertaking for some time yet. An easy way is to clean one room each day, just picking up a bit in the rest of the house. If you have a large house, shut off any rooms you don't have to use.

Any woman suffers when she becomes a social recluse, but be careful about having too many guests in these early months. When people drop in for the evening—you definitely should not have any dinner guests for a while—buy cookies and serve them with coffee for refreshment, or serve cheese and crackers. Arrange snacks so that the guests can help themselves; you will be too tired to enjoy company if you have to spend the evening waiting on people. And since a good night's sleep is not a luxury but a necessity for you, make your excuses and go to bed when you are sleepy. At least, retire to the couch and toss out your conversational gems from a horizontal position. Sooner or later, visitors will get the idea of arranging to come early and leave early.

How Much Clothing?

Dress the baby simply. If you maintain the room temperatures we have suggested, a shirt and diaper are usually enough in the daytime, and a shirt and diaper with nightgown over them are usually enough at night when he is bundled under the covers. If it is very hot, replace the shirt with a loose-fitting kimono-type garment.

For if the baby's skin is damp with perspiration, the least breath of cool air may chill him. (You know how you feel when your blouse is damp and you find yourself in a draft.) To protect a tiny baby from this type of chilling, it is best to keep a loose garment over his shoulders even in hot weather. (But cotton, please, not wool.) When he is older—say around six months—and it is hot, a diaper only will do.

Feel the baby to see if he is too hot or too cold, and dress him according to the thermometer, not the calendar. If his body is warm and his feet and hands only barely cool, he is all right. If his body is wet, he is too hot. Take off any extras you have on him. If his hands and feet are cold, not just barely cool, he is chilly and needs more clothing.

There is a natural temptation to put too much clothing on a baby, because he seems so little and fragile. The result is that he perspires profusely and then is likely to become chilled. The fact is that babies often need less clothing, comparatively speaking, than adults to be comfortable. Watch and feel your baby and you will dress him suitably. And remember that the less often you dress him up in finery, the less laundry you will have.

Airings

A baby born in the summer may go outdoors by the time he is a week or ten days old. Newborns should not be exposed to sudden temperature changes, so winter babies are better off in the house until they are at least a month old. After that time, the winter baby can have his naps out of doors if you have a porch and the weather is not too inclement. Do not overdress the baby for his outings. Feel him now and then. If his body is wet with perspiration, you have too many clothes or wrappings on him.

Exercise Periods

As the baby stays awake for longer periods, give him plenty of time to exercise on a large, padded surface. It isn't too soon to get a play pen, but you can use your own bed for the exercising if you haven't a play pen yet. Place something that is waterproof over the spread, but be sure to see that he is guarded so he can't roll off. Part of the exercise time he should be allowed to play alone and amuse himself, but part of the time it is fun for his parents to play with him. He loves to have his back rubbed, and he dotes on mild roughhousing. It is not a good idea, though, to get him excited just before or just after eating or to play hard enough to bounce his meal right out, or shake him up so he'll have difficulty digesting it.

In his exercise periods don't try to hurry along his development. If you have read that some month-old babies hold their heads up very well and yours doesn't yet, forget it. He will hold his head up when he is good and ready; by trying to force him now, you may weaken rather than strengthen muscles.

Sun Baths

Summer babies may be given sun baths by the time they are a month to ten weeks old. The sun is usually at its hottest by June 21st. The farther south you live, the more intense the sun's rays are. Summer noonday sun is too hot for babies. Generally speaking, an exposure of one to two minutes between 9:00 and 11:00 A.M. or 2:00 and 5:00 P.M. is safe as a starter. But the sun varies in intensity according to season, latitude, and time of day, so it is best to ask your doctor how long it is safe to expose your baby in a particular month in your location.

Take all the baby's clothes off, including his diaper, and place a clean folded diaper under him. Keep his head in the shade at first and toast him on his front, then on his back. Gradually increase the time of exposure to the sun, adding no more than four minutes a day, until he can remain in it for half an hour—fifteen minutes on each side. This is a baby's maximum, even if he is nicely tanned. Let him lie on a cotton pad in the open; it usually gets too hot for him inside a carriage or bassinet. Always protect your baby's eyes from direct glare. Place him so that his face is turned away from the sun. A fair-haired baby should wear a hat.

Winter babies, of course, have to wait for milder weather to be allowed to kick unclothed in the outdoor air. Consult your doctor for the proper time and age to start sun baths.

Visits to the Doctor

The doctor will tell you when to bring the baby to the office for the first visit. As a rule, it is when the baby is six weeks old (at which time you must be examined by your doctor, too), but since there is a trend nowadays to add foods to Baby's diet at an earlier age, you will have to ask your pediatrician or general physician about this.

If possible, have your husband go with you. You'll be glad to have his help in carrying the baby, and it's nice for him to hear at firsthand what the doctor says and to ask the questions that occur to him. Plan well for these visits to the doctor. Be sure to take an extra diaper or two with you, and don't dress the baby in fussy clothes. You will have to take everything off for the doctor's examination, and tugging elaborate clothing off and then on again will make your visits to the doctor more of an ordeal for yourself and the baby than they need to be.

It is an excellent plan to keep a notebook in which you can jot down questions as they occur to you. Take it with you to the doctor's office and jot down his replies. That way you won't forget important things.

The doctor will weigh and measure your baby and examine him from the top of his head to his toes. He will then make suggestions about the way to care for the little fellow until the time for the next visit. The doctor wants to help you, so don't hesitate to question him about anything that is bothering you. Part of the doctor's job is educating you in the ways of babies.

Starting Vitamins

By the time your baby is two weeks old, the doctor will probably have started him on vitamins C and D. These are often prescribed in a commercial preparation also containing vitamin A. Vitamin D is needed throughout the growing period; vitamin C is not stored by the body and must be replenished daily. These two vitamins are necessary for both bottle-fed and breast-fed babies.

Opened bottles of vitamins must be tightly capped and stored in the refrigerator. The baby doesn't mind taking the solution cold. It can be given from a spoon, but the easier way is to fill the dropper that comes with the bottle to the prescribed amount (the dropper is marked), slip it into the corner of Baby's mouth, and gently squeeze. Hold his lips closed until he swallows. Babies don't dislike the taste, but at first they have a little trouble swallowing anything that does not come from a nipple.

Orange or other fruit juice fortified with vitamin C may be started in the baby's second month. Don't heat it, as heat destroys vitamin C. Dilute a teaspoon of juice with a teaspoon of boiled, cooled water. If it agrees with the baby, increase the amount gradually. Until he is taking two or three ounces of undiluted juice, the doctor will want you to continue with his vitamin C drops. The juice may be given from a spoon or bottle at first, then from a cup. Canned-for-baby juices are prepared for easy digestibility.

Starting Solid Foods

The doctor will also tell you when to start solid foods and what foods to begin with. (Some doctors begin these at three months, some earlier.) If it is cereal, you will be very pleased with the variety available in ready-cooked baby cereals. You just add warm milk or water and serve. The first time you offer it, make it mostly milk so that it is very thin. Start with small amounts, feeding only a little at a time, using a small spoon.

It may take the baby two weeks or more before he begins to enjoy it. But, it is much more important that you be relaxed and unworried when you start something new with your baby than that he eat a certain amount of food by a certain age. He senses immediately any changes in your emotions and he reacts to them. If you are upset for some reason, he will connect it with this funny new stuff you are putting in his mouth, and he will naturally be afraid of the food. If you don't care whether he eats it or not that day, he soon will be eating it. If he rejects it violently, wait a while before offering it again.

Wait Till Baby's Good-natured

If the baby has a cold or for some other reason isn't his normal self, wait until the situation is all cleared up before you start him on new foods. Continue giving him the cereal in a rather liquid state until he accepts the new taste, then every day or so add a little more cereal to the milk. The consistency to arrive at should resemble pea soup or thin mashed potatoes.

If your baby does not take a liking to one food as a starter, the doctor will suggest another. Some doctors start with fruit because almost all babies love the taste. All fruits for a baby must be cooked and strained, with the exception of banana. If fully ripe, this can be well mashed and fed to the baby. Scrape off the thin stringy coating under the skin before mashing. Banana also comes in the baby foods, of course—all of which are ready-prepared for Baby to eat. When you introduce a new food to the baby, give him just a taste at first. At every meal, give him no more than he wants—with no coaxing.

Canned Foods Are Such a Help

You probably know all about the canned baby foods you buy in stores. These are a great aid to the mother. The food is of the best quality and is already strained, properly seasoned for the infant, and sterilized. When you consider the time and energy spent in cooking and laboriously straining meats, fruits, and vegetables in the home, and the tremendous amount of waste involved, you will see that the canned baby foods are very economical and a real boon to mothers. Among the many brands of canned food for babies, you will be able to find any fruit, vegetable, meat, or pudding you want, as well as soups, various mixtures, and soft, sieved egg yolk.

Occasionally you will cook something for the baby—applesauce or puddings. Babies and small children don't require as much sweetening as adults usually do, so put in less sugar than you would in cooking the same thing for adults. If he doesn't like it that way, you can always add a bit of sugar. The same goes for salt—less is required by children—and no spices should be given for several years.

Baby Likes It Warm and Cozy

Baby will enjoy his food served warm. (In hot weather, room temperature is warm enough.) Perhaps you have one of those baby dishes with a compartment on the bottom for hot water that warms the food. There are also electrically warmed dishes that simplify mother's work even more. The divisions in baby dishes are especially helpful when Baby starts to feed himself. Some have bottoms that anchor the dish to the feeding table.

When you start Baby on spoon-fed foods, hold him on your lap and try to make him feel as cozy as he does when you are feeding him his milk. This way, the strange new way of eating will be more acceptable to him. Eating from a spoon is quite different from sucking on a nipple. He has to learn how to move the food back in his mouth to swallow it. At first, most of it may come oozing out. Give him tiny bites—and plenty of time and patience.

Fitting In New Foods

The best time to give orange juice and vitamins is right before the bath, when the baby's clothes are removed. Juice stains are hard to scrub out of clothing.

If the baby is drinking breast milk, don't give him his cereal at the 6:00 A.M. feeding, since this is the feeding when he gets more milk than at any other time of day. However, he is usually happiest in the mornings, so the 10:00 A.M. feeding is a good time to start cereal. Give him a taste before his milk. If he is vehement about turning it down, give him enough milk to take the edge off his hunger before you offer the cereal. Experiment with him until you find the psychological time to present it to him.

In spite of all we've said about not overdoing, you may be very tired at the day's end and may not have much milk in your breasts at the 6:00 P.M. feeding. Once the baby has learned to like cereal, you can give it to him at 6:00 after he has finished his milk. If he hasn't been sleeping through the night, he probably will start now and wake up in the morning in a less starved condition.

Fruits and vegetables are usually given first with the 2:00 P.M. milk, then added to the evening meal.

Accomplishments

We hope you have noticed that "maybe" and "perhaps" and "probably" are used over and over again in this book. That is because no two babies are exactly alike, and what is normal behavior for one child is not necessarily normal for another. This applies to accomplishments, too. The only reason we are going to list accomplishments is to give you a general idea of what your baby will be doing next. Don't use the list to check up on him, because he doesn't know anything about a list and will do things in his own way.

If we say that some babies smile at the age of two months, note that we say "some babies," not "all smart babies." The thing for you to do is not to care whether *your* baby smiles at four weeks, eight weeks, or twelve weeks; when he does, smile right back at him and be glad that the funny little creature is so happy he feels like showing it.

Maybe (there's that word again) your baby will smile early and laugh late. So what? That's all right, too.

With all that advance briefing, we tell you with trepidation that many babies, by the time they are about three months old:

1. React to noises, first by giving a start, later by looking in the direction of the noise.
2. Get better control of their eyes, first by turning them toward light, later by watching people.
3. Smile.
4. Seem to recognize Mother or Father.
5. Hold up their heads.
6. Reach toward objects.

Whatever your baby does or doesn't do, if he is healthy and happy, eating as he should, and growing in consequence, you are carrying out your part of the job, and by this time you'll feel like an experienced hand at it. If someone were to ask you now about those first-week fears and anxieties, we wager you'd answer, "What fears?"

CHAPTER SEVEN

Three to six months

Three to six months is still a period of rapid growth and increasing appetite. You can see a personality now when you watch your baby, not just a helpless little bundle. He is just about the right size, too, for cuddling. Make the most of this, because soon he won't hold still long enough to cuddle.

He welcomes his juice and vitamins with great gusto and probably is already getting accustomed to solid food. If the doctor hasn't advised giving him solids until now, you can go back to page 60 for hints on how to go about it. With each new food, start out in the same gradual way, with just a taste at first. If the child smacks his lips over the first taste, you can give him more, but since his digestive apparatus has to get used to handling the new food, allow him not more than a level tablespoonful on the first day. All the canned baby foods agree with most babies, but sometimes a vegetable causes loose bowel movements, and spinach will occasionally make the baby's buttocks look red and tender. If a reaction of this kind occurs, increase the amount of this vegetable very slowly. If the child seems uncomfortable, stop it entirely for a month or so. Occasionally, beets turn the stool, and more rarely the urine, red. Red urine should always be reported to the doctor, but also tell him if your baby has been eating beets. There is an even chance that every food will come out the same color as it went in for a while; don't let it alarm you.

Give a Disliked Food a Rest

Even if some fruit or vegetable agrees with the baby, but he just doesn't like it, don't insist. Don't offer it again for a few weeks; he may develop a great liking for it then. It is a good idea to have a food of which he is particularly fond on his plate at the same time you offer something new or something he has refused before. If you give them in alternate bites, he may forget all about his dislike for the latter. In giving new foods to the baby, do it in such a way that you can tell whether or not one disagrees with him. Let's say that the doctor mentions applesauce as a likely starter, introduced gradually. After about four days of applesauce with no ill effects, you can be pretty sure it is all right for him. Then add a bite or so of strained stewed pears (or any other cooked fruit), dropping applesauce entirely the next day. Give him pears for a couple of days more, and if there is no trouble, introduce a third fruit. Handle vegetables in the same way. Put the remainder in the refrigerator, to be used the following day, but discard any left after that time. Three days in a row for one can is too long. If an opened can was left out of the refrigerator overnight, discard it.

There Are Lots of Ways

Different doctors have different ways of introducing new foods into the baby's eating schedule, and of course you will follow your own doctor's advice about this. He may suggest that fruit be given first at the 2:00 P.M. feeding or its equivalent, and then after a few weeks switched to the supper hour. He may advise vegetables and meat for the 2:00 P.M. feeding also, and then later the addition of a vegetable to the supper menu. In this way you work gradually toward the idea of three meals a day. However, there is no hard and fast rule about this, and it doesn't matter particularly so long as the baby's food list is constantly growing.

Giving Egg Yolks

Egg yolks are usually given when the baby is about five months old, but this is to be decided, as always, by the doctor. Some babies are allergic to eggs, so these have to be introduced with care. Soft, sieved egg yolk is available in prepared-for-baby foods. Or you can hard-cook an egg, then remove and sieve the yolk. Mix about one-quarter teaspoon of the sieved yolk with a little milk, enough to make it easy for your baby to swallow. If the baby is happy and undisturbed the next day, give him another tiny amount the same way. Egg yolk should be increased very gradually to be sure it does not cause a reaction. If the baby develops a rash or digestive disturbance, give him no more egg yolk for a couple of months, and then start all over. Only after he has been eating an egg yolk for two or three months do you begin to add, very gradually, the egg white. Egg is a valuable addition to your baby's diet; it supplies iron and vitamins as well as protein. A baby who cannot eat eggs should eat an extra amount of other foods which supply these nutriments. Later, most children get so they can take eggs, even though allergic to them at first.

A Tooth in the Offing

When your baby begins to drool a lot and perhaps to chew on everything he can get into his mouth, you know that the long process of teething has started. It may be months before the first tooth appears, but by six months he can gnaw on a piece of toast or zwieback or a teething biscuit. It makes him happy to have a piece of toast while you are eating your breakfast.

Weaning from the Breast

With each new food you have been adding, you have been weaning your baby to a certain extent. Some mothers who have plenty of milk like to continue nursing their babies, and there are stories of nursing carried on for unusual lengths of time. Doctors usually advise that a year is long enough, and in the days before bottle feedings nine months was considered a good time to stop.

Quite often, the milk supply will begin to fail around the sixth month. Or, as your baby acquires teeth, he may be so hard on your nipples that you will feel it is time to stop nursing regardless.

Breast feeding may have to be discontinued for any number of reasons.

If Sudden Weaning Is Necessary

Your doctor will suggest a formula, which you make according to the directions on pages 45-47. If you make a twenty-four-hour supply of formula, you should take all the usual precautions with regard to sterilization. But if it is a simple formula—just evaporated milk and water, with perhaps a little sweetening—which you prefer to prepare separately for each meal, ask your doctor if you have to sterilize all the paraphernalia involved. If he says not, be sure anyway that everything is very clean and has been rinsed with boiling water.

If you have to wean suddenly, offer formula to the baby at each feeding time, giving him the breasts only when they are too full to be comfortable. Cut down your liquid intake and your milk will soon be gone.

But Better to Do It Gradually

Ordinarily, however, when there are no emergency circumstances, it is wisest to wean gradually. Give him a bottle at the feeding when he gets the least milk from you, probably at 6:00 P.M. When your breasts have adapted themselves to this decrease in output, eliminate the next most convenient feeding and give the baby a bottle instead. Continue with this until all breast feedings have been dropped. The early-morning feeding will probably be the last to go.

Perhaps you would like to continue to nurse your baby, but your milk supply is insufficient and your doctor has told you to supplement the nursings with formula. In this case, have your baby empty the breast before giving him the bottle. Maybe your baby has been nursing from one breast only at a feeding. Have him empty both before giving the extra milk.

You Might Offer a Cup

With a baby of five or six months, it does no harm to offer formula in a cup once a day, at a time when he is usually happy.

When he grows proficient and seems to prefer drinking from a cup, it is all right to drop both breast and bottle feedings. He should be pampered in his feeding preferences because he is expressing a need—either for more sucking satisfaction or for more love and cuddling with a resulting feeling of security. Never force the cup and do not get upset if it takes some time to win the baby over. Give him an attractive cup that is all his own, offering him milk in it once each day. If he develops a violent hatred for the cup, put it away for two weeks and then bring it out again. Eventually, he will begin to use it, and he will do it sooner if you are calm and relaxed.

Family Playtime

You will want to get a play pen for your baby. These come in many styles at various prices, but all you really need is a pen strong enough to withstand the jumping and shaking of your little Hercules. It will be worth its weight in gold, because you can place it indoors or out, knowing that your baby will be safe while you go about your chores. In it the baby can play, exercise, watch the world pass by, and learn to amuse himself. Placed in a pen at an early age, he will usually play happily in it when he is older instead of hanging onto your skirts and getting tangled up in your feet while you try to clean house.

Over the bottom of the pen should be laid a pad. Pads made from oilcloth or plastic material are easiest to keep clean, but anything, such as an old quilt, will do if you wash it often. Place a few toys inside and put the pen in an interesting location. When outdoors, a baby likes to be where he can watch people, but well enough away from the sidewalk so that passers-by won't come up and touch him. In the house he likes to be where he can keep an eye on Mother as she attends to her various duties.

Keep the Play Pen Fun

Don't insist that the baby stay in his pen for too long a period. Lift him when he becomes really discontented, as you want him to think of the play pen as a pleasant place to be. Be sure that he has enough toys to amuse him for a while, and he soon will be spending a considerable part of his waking time there. As an additional attraction, you can give him a piece of toast when you put him in the pen. Babies firmly believe that anything connected with food is a bit of all right.

Even though you have a convenient place to park your baby at times, he still needs to be played with. In fact, as he grows older, family playtime becomes more and more important to him. Play music for him now and then on the radio or phonograph. He likes to have you tell him little stories, although he can't understand the words. He loves to have you squeeze his squeaky toys and roll balls to him. The play is one-sided at first, with you doing all the work, but you can see that he is obviously having a wonderful time.

Should Dad Be Curbed?

Fathers are sometimes criticized for expressing their love and interest by tossing the baby into the air and handling him generally as though he were a basketball. Usually the baby highly approves this treatment, and there is no harm in it, provided Father doesn't get too rough. So don't worry. It is legitimate to suggest, however, that there be no roughhousing just after a meal or just before bedtime. If this kind of play makes you nervous, busy yourself in another room and let father and child have their romp. The baby is your husband's, too, and within reason he has a right to have fun with him in a father's way. Wisdom is not the exclusive property of mothers. Fathers, nowadays, know a thing or two about babies also.

In connection with playtime, and any other time, you should always lift the baby by his body and never by his arms, or you may place too much strain on his shoulders. It is all right to lift him when he is holding on to your hands, his body tensed and ready.

Accomplishments

Again we stress the point that you should not expect your child to do a certain thing at any set age. But by the time he is six months old you can begin to look for the following stages of development:

1. Attempting to sit up. He may be able to hold a sitting position when he is propped up against pillows; if not, don't risk weakening his back by forcing the issue.
2. Recognizing people he sees often, besides his mother and father, and refusing to go to strangers.
3. Better muscle coordination, ability to pick up things and drop them at will. He loves to throw toys from the play pen, then wants them back immediately.
4. Excellent vision. He likes flowers, other brightly colored things.
5. Playing like a kitten with paper, rattling it, pouncing on it, tearing it, trying to eat it.
6. Trying to roll over. May succeed and then not do it again for many weeks.
7. Laughing aloud.
8. Making swimming motions when placed on the floor–sometimes actually moving quite a distance by wriggles.

Toys

Around the age of three months he may be ready for a rattle –it won't hurt to get one, anyway. It should be of sturdy construction and of a material that can be boiled. During this three-to-six-months period, babies get increasing enjoyment from animals of cloth or rubber that can be washed; rag or rubber dolls; soft balls about 3 inches in diameter and hence not too big for them to grasp. As the baby's eyes learn to focus and as he gets more command over his movements, he will like to hit at bright-colored objects suspended over his crib–but do be sure that any apparatus of this kind is fastened tight at each end.

You can help the baby to develop imagination and resource by providing him with a variety of materials to do things with, homely household things that will challenge his ingenuity as he gets older. Around six months, for instance, he will have wonderful times crumpling colored paper, playing with pasteboard boxes and cartons, experimenting with the possibilities of a pillow. Do not give him a great many toys at any one time, however. Keep some in reserve, to bring out when he tires of the old stand-bys.

Babies particularly love to look at themselves in a mirror. By the time of the half-year birthday, it will probably be quite a chore to diaper your little wriggler. If you keep a mirror handy—one on which he can't hurt himself—his own image will keep him fascinatedly quiet until you have his diaper on.

Nothing should be given a baby that cannot be chewed or licked with impunity; nothing should be given that has sharp edges or that will come apart in little pieces which the baby might swallow.

CHAPTER EIGHT

Six to nine months

Now that the baby is getting a larger variety and quantity of solid foods, he is able to go for longer periods of time without eating. We said before that with the addition of solids he would begin working toward a three-meal-per-day schedule. This, like everything else, won't happen overnight or at any set time. It may be that your baby has already made the switch; perhaps he won't be ready for some time. There is no need to hurry him, but you can be manipulating things a bit in that direction.

When would you like the baby to eat his breakfast? If you decide on 7:30 A.M., for example, give the baby his milk at 6:00 A.M., or whenever he is in the habit of proclaiming his hunger. If this doesn't tide him over until 7:30, a piece of buttered toast will. Maybe at first he will have to be fed at 7:00, but you can soon help him reach the later time over a period of days. Eventually, he will be able to do without the early milk and eat his entire breakfast at 7:30—cereal, milk, egg yolk, and toast.

Breakfast over, return him to bed for as long as he will stay there happily, and then bathe him.

Midmorning Snack

His juice, vitamins, and crackers in midmorning, as usual, plus another issue of milk if he still wants a 9:00 or 10:00 o'clock helping, will fill his tummy enough to wait for a meal at noon. Thus, the 10:00 and 2:00 o'clock feedings merge gradually into a lunch given at 12:00 (or at 11:30 if you have to feed a husband or older children at 12:00).

After lunch, the baby will be ready for a second nap. When he awakes from this, he will probably accept enthusiastically zwieback or arrowroot cookies and milk.

Later, when he is hungry, you can give him his supper of cooked fruit, cereal or pudding, and an egg yolk if he didn't eat one for breakfast. He may want this meal at 6:00 or at 5:00. Let him be the judge.

During this period of transition to three meals a day, it doesn't matter when the baby drinks his milk, so long as he gets at least twenty ounces a day. We don't mean by this that you can give him milk so immediately before a meal that it will spoil his appetite, but it is permissible to eliminate milk at lunch if he drank about seven ounces in the middle of the morning. Later, his needs will change and he will have milk at mealtime. We repeat that a schedule like this should be reached gradually. If the baby cries for milk at 10:00 A.M. and has little appetite at 12:00 for his solids, he isn't ready for a three-meal-a-day regime.

Bowel Training Now?

After the baby can sit alone (but not before) and if his bowel movements come at a regular time, you can usually see that he has his movement in whatever toilet arrangement you have for him, if you wish to do this.

You must understand, however, that it is purely reflex action that prompts him to move his bowels when he is placed on a toilet seat or chair at such an early age. He is not nearly advanced enough to realize what he is doing or what is expected of him. Your only reason for attempting to do away now with movements in his diapers is to keep him clean and to avoid washing soiled napkins.

There is no harm in putting him on a toilet seat at this age, if you go about it with a relaxed attitude, not really expecting to succeed and not really caring if you don't. If the baby's bowels move at a certain time each day—8:00 A.M., for instance—set him on his toilet chair when the hour rolls around or when he begins to grunt. Never leave him on the toilet for more than a few minutes, and if he is unhappy, take him off at once. If you are lucky, one of these days he may have a movement in the toilet. After a while, his bowels may automatically move when he feels the toilet seat against his buttocks. But remember that they will also automatically move when he has to go, toilet seat or no toilet seat. Don't blame him for any lapses. It will be months before he can grasp the association between elimination and toilets.

Many specialists in child care feel that it is better to wait for toilet training until after a child is eighteen months old, or whenever he himself expresses an interest in using a toilet seat. With one child it might be before he is eighteen months old, with another child it might be when he is two and a half. We discuss the proper procedure with the older baby on page 160. If you decide you want to try earlier, bear in mind the fact that any success you have may be temporary. You'll probably have it all to do again later. And if there has been any strain or unpleasantness at this time, it will be harder to help the baby train himself when he is truly old enough. Of course, you will postpone any attempts to train him until he is over a cold, you are feeling well and relaxed, and Baby's routine is otherwise running smoothly.

Teething

It is impossible to predict when the first tooth will erupt. Sometimes an unfortunate infant has tender gums for months before the transparent tooth rim is seen. Another baby may exhibit no signs whatsoever, the first inkling you have of the great event being the clicking sound of tooth against spoon. Around the sixth month is a usual time, but don't worry if your baby is dentally unproductive at a year. (We thought our second baby *never* would get teeth, but she did.) When he is restless, unhappy, and the doctor can find nothing physically wrong, the child is probably having a bad time with his teeth.

When he spends most of his time chewing on thumbs or toys

or the furniture, give him a hard-rubber teething ring, and perhaps a smooth bone, such as a drumstick, but with no splinters that may make trouble. (During this time of chewing, make sure he can't get hold of anything that will injure him.) Rubbing the gums with a clean finger may give him relief. If he wakes crying several times in the night, change him and hold him a little while until he can sleep again. Maybe all that's needed is to bring his bed right next to yours for a few nights, where you can reach over and pat him when he cries, until he is sleeping well again.

If he has a fever or diarrhea or any other physical symptom, consult the doctor. Teething does not cause illness. When a baby's restlessness is caused by teething, usually the gums are red and swollen. If there is no evidence of irritation in the gums, it is wise to seek some other reason for irritability or unhappiness.

Accomplishments

By the time your baby reaches his ninth month, he may be doing all or some of the following things:

1. Sitting up. Some babies, usually fatter ones, will have a hard time assuming the sitting position for several months yet, but once they are seated they can hold the pose easily.
2. Rolling over. There is trouble with this also if the baby is heavy. Or maybe he just doesn't want to.
3. Adding consonants to his speech. "Da da," "Ga ga," and so forth.
4. Moving rhythmically to music. Sometimes with his entire body, sometimes just the head or arms or legs.
5. Creeping. There are almost as many ways of creeping and crawling as there are babies. If yours develops a rare, unorthodox way of self-propulsion, let him do it that way. Some babies don't creep at all; they just wait a while longer than their brothers before they try locomotion, then stand up and walk one fine day.

When He Begins to Creep

When your baby begins to creep, remove from his reach anything with sharp points or other harmful characteristics. But in each room do place a few objects that belong to him, always keeping them in the same place so he will know where to find them. If possible, have a room reserved for him where he can crawl around and play with no restrictions whatsoever. A sound-making push toy or other favorite plaything placed just beyond his reach will stimulate his efforts.

Block off with chairs or gates all dangerous places such as hot radiators, stairways, and electric outlets, and then leave him alone. Yes, he's bound to have a few bumps and falls. But they are part of his education. He will soon learn good balance and how to avoid being hurt. When he has a slight accident, speak to him in a comforting but matter-of-fact voice, telling him he is all right. You will know immediately from his cry if the bump was hard enough to require a little session of love and sympathy.

He'll Meet Frustrations

At first he will meet with many frustrations, and it is your job to show him how to overcome them. He may crawl into a corner —and cry because he doesn't know how to get out. Help him back out or turn around, whichever way he seems to understand better, and after a few such incidents he will remember how to do it all by himself. He may pull himself up on a low footstool and then not know how to get down again. Show him how to let his feet down slowly until they touch the floor, speaking encouragingly to him. After you have helped him out of the same situation dozens of times and he still lacks the initiative to try it himself, just leave him alone to solve the situation. Once he sees it is up to him, he will manage quite nicely, though perhaps a bit resentfully. Some babies seem to be born with the philosophy of "letting George do it"; their mothers must stifle the urge to give too much assistance, once it is plain that the baby is capable of handling his problem.

Traveling with a Baby

Perhaps the necessity of traveling has arisen earlier in your baby's life; but since we feel that a baby is better off at home for the first six months, we are inserting it here. Before planning to take your baby on a trip at any age, ask your doctor about it first. Even at six months, a trip with a baby is no small undertaking. However, it is true that after the initial preparations, many parents find traveling with their baby little trouble, and enjoyable for all. Some say a trip is easier with a young baby who sleeps most of the time.

The secret of success is advance preparation.

Now is the time really to take advantage of commercial aids. Buy disposable diapers. If you are to be away for only a few days, use these exclusively; if the trip is to be a long one, use them at least during the time spent traveling, and make use of diaper liners with your regular diapers. If your baby is on a formula, you will find plastic bottles or disposable bottles a great convenience.

Bottle Management

If you are traveling by plane or train, you can ask the porter or stewardess to put a day's supply of regular bottles of formula in the refrigerator, and heat one for you as needed. If you travel by car, you can take a day's supply in a portable icebox. However, it is difficult to sterilize bottles and to mix a new supply of formula. It is better to take along small cans of evaporated milk or one of the several brands of prepared formula (ask your doctor to recommend one). All you will then need will be bottles containing the proper proportion of sterile water (mixed with sweetening, if required) which you can fill with the proper amount of milk or prepared formula. Mix only enough formula for each feeding. If you take ready-to-use prepared formula, bring bottles which have been sterilized at home. A car bottle warmer can also be used to heat jars and cans of prepared baby food.

A porter or stewardess will also heat canned baby foods for you. If you are going by car, either discard the unused portion after each meal or keep it in a portable ice box. You can give the baby bottled orange juice, as it is government inspected, and you can buy it everywhere. Or you can take along small cans of baby orange juice. Don't forget a can opener.

Traveling is sometimes hard on a nursing mother, causing her milk supply temporarily to diminish. Before you leave, ask your doctor for a fill-in formula in case this happens to you. Since the baby's schedule will be upset anyhow in traveling, it probably will be better for him (and for your nerves) to give him a complementary bottle for a day or two if he isn't getting enough from you.

Carrier a Help

If you are going on the train, a portable baby carrier, a basket, or a car bed for naps will be a great help. Many necessities can be tucked in around the edges. You should carry a separate small suitcase for the baby's belongings, and a waterproof bag for soiled diapers and clothing. You will need several changes of clothing for him. And you should plan to wear something that will stand soil or mussing, for traveling with a baby is a messy business. And keep a supply of cleansing tissues handy—their uses are countless.

If you are driving, safety authorities point out that a baby is much safer in a car bed or seat than on your lap, and that the back seat is safer than the front. These items are practically a necessity for the baby traveler. Just be sure they are securely anchored. A car seat enables the baby who is big enough to sit up to see the scenery and passing cars. There are several different types. Most of them are collapsible for easy carrying. A car seat can double as a feeding chair. You can see how handy it would be in restaurants and in homes where you are visiting.

Play Pen if Possible

A play pen is a great help. Often you will find that other people's homes are filled with breakable gadgets very tempting to a baby who isn't old enough to understand the rules of mine and thine. Too, in a strange place among strange people, some babies stick to their mammas like adhesive tape. His play pen with a few of his very own toys will amuse him for a while, giving you a chance to breathe freely. He can sleep in his play pen if necessary. A number of models convert to cribs; some convert to dressing tables as well.

Include waterproof sheeting among your list of necessities, as the baby may have to be changed on someone else's couch. Baby's favorite cuddle toy for bedtime and one of his favorite blankets (many babies grow very attached to one blanket in particular and can't sleep without it) will help him adjust to new sleeping arrangements.

Keep a Flexible Schedule

Obviously, you will have to make many changes in your baby's schedule. Observe it as much as you can and don't worry. If your trip is short and you find that the schedule is impossible to follow, concentrate on keeping the baby comfortable and yourself happy. When you return home and the baby is once more in familiar surroundings, he will automatically go back to his accustomed regime. He tends to associate a certain way of living with familiar rooms and furniture.

On an extended trip, however, it is best to have a schedule and to follow it from the first. Since your schedule has always been flexible anyway, you can certainly do some shifting around, but once you discover the most convenient way to manage, stick to it as closely as circumstances permit.

Kindness to Relatives

If you are staying with relatives or friends, you will want everything to go as smoothly as possible. You are proud of your baby, but don't be touchy about him or your methods. And don't believe all you hear about in-law trouble and meddling grandparents. Don't take it for granted that your family is going to interfere; as a matter of fact, most grandparents today are pretty well acquainted with modern baby-care methods. Remember that your baby is a member of the family and that your relatives are naturally intensely interested in his welfare. Listen to any suggestions and comments without resentment. Some of them you will be able to use, some not.

If any of your methods of caring for the baby are criticized, explain why you do things the way you do, replying that you are following your doctor's advice and that your system works very well. If you are nice about it and your baby is a healthy specimen, your critic will soon see for himself or herself the advantages of your methods.

When to Be Firm

You should be firm about the baby's schedule and not let him be deprived of his daily nap or early bedtime. If he misses his regular sleep, he will soon become cross and unhappy. But arrange for most of his regular waking hours to be spent in the company of his grandparents or other relatives. And as soon as the baby knows them and feels secure with them, go off and give them some time alone together. A little so-called "spoiling" from grandparents and other admirers is wonderful for a baby. If the baby's new friends are allowed leeway in handling him, they will be glad to abide by a few of your hard and fast rules.

The main thing for you to do when traveling with a baby is to take things as they come and not get upset over things you can do nothing about. Try to plan beforehand so that you can carry out your trip in the smoothest way possible. You will probably be kept twice as busy as at home, but if the trip is worth taking, you can make it enjoyable for everyone concerned by good management.

CHAPTER NINE

Nine to twelve months

After your baby has worked his way to a three-meal day, with perhaps some help from you, the schedule will remain much the same for a while. There is one change that is likely to take place, however, in the period you are now entering. During the second half of the first year, a baby usually gets over its special need to suck, which we noted earlier. Somewhere between six and eight months, therefore, the bottle baby can gradually be accustomed to sips of milk out of a cup though still having most of it by bottle. Remember that some infants continue their need to suck longer than others. When a baby seems to be still emotionally bound up with his bottle, ask your doctor's advice before starting to wean him.

However, if your baby has been taking some liquids from a cup and has no objection to this method, he is probably ready to begin the weaning process. By this time, the normal baby is usually able to take milk unmodified, but ask your doctor if it should still be boiled. If your baby has been on an evaporated-milk formula, you can continue the evaporated milk. Four ounces of evaporated milk and four ounces of warm water will give you the equivalent of a glass of fresh milk.

Let Him Get Acquainted with Cup

If your baby has not used a cup, accustom him to it before you try substituting it for his bottle. Put a plastic cup of pretty color on his tray at each meal, with nothing in it. He can handle it as he likes and get thoroughly used to it. Then at each meal put a small amount of milk in the cup and let him drink this. Finish with the bottle. Gradually increase the amount of milk in the cup. When he is taking enough for his needs, retire the bottles from service.

A violent reaction against the cup is a signal to wait a while. Some babies will take milk willingly from the cup except at the last feeding of the day, when they still want the bottle. Modern doctors do not deny this last bottle, when the baby clings to it, up to the age of eighteen months or thereabouts. Then it is advised that the final stage of weaning be done in loving fashion, holding the toddler on one's lap and cuddling him while persuading him to take his nightcap from a cup.

Eating Patterns Changing?

The first six months are a period of such rapid growth, and hence of such rapidly increasing appetite, that you may be concerned if your baby now begins to want less food or to seem finicky about it.

Perhaps you have been giving him his milk first at each mealtime, and that temporarily fills him up, taking away tummy room for solid foods. Habits are hard to break, so you may have to continue giving him some milk first, but just a little. Then after he has eaten all the solids he wants, let him have more milk. Often when babies are getting used to the three-meal-a-day regime, they cut down on milk intake. Occasionally, they even develop a dislike for milk. If yours does, the best thing to do is humor him—by taking the milk away if he refuses it. Make up for this by using more milk in his cooked foods. Give him creamed soup, creamed vegetables, milk puddings, mild cheese. All he needs is a change; after a while he will drink milk willingly once more. Avoid sweetening or flavoring his glass of milk; it is better that he get less milk for a few weeks than develop an unnecessary taste for sweetened milk.

Something to Chew On

When a baby begins getting teeth, he wants to chew and he should be given every encouragement in it. As we mentioned in the preceding chapter, he is going to chew something, regardless of what it is. When he has enough teeth to do a fairly effective job of chewing, start him on chopped foods. Begin with a favorite food, and buy two jars or cans—one of the junior variety and one of the strained. If he balks at a lump, give him another bite of strained food. Don't rush him.

He may be intrigued by the appearance of chopped banana or a piece of macaroni and try to pick it up with his fingers. If he does, you should be pleased, because this is a first step toward feeding himself. Supply him with bits of food he *can* pick up. Some of the dry cereals come in small pieces that are still big enough for a baby to grasp easily. Put a dozen or so pieces on his tray and let him play with them. He'll soon discover they are good. Pieces of vegetable, cooked until they are soft, often intrigue him long before he will accept chopped food from a spoon. These will be easier for him to handle if you wipe them off with a paper napkin so that they aren't slippery. Pieces of hard-boiled egg and of finely ground meat or baby meat sticks are also easy for him to manage with his fingers, and they encourage him to chew.

As soon as he is used to one type of chopped food, introduce another. All the canned chopped baby foods are suitable for him and can be digested even if the baby still hasn't any teeth.

First Attempts at Self-feeding

Whenever he takes an interest in self-feeding, encourage him. He will be messy at first, smearing the food all over himself, his high chair, and the floor. It will take him weeks to master the spoon (a baby spoon is easier for him to handle), and he will swoop up his glass of milk with a grand gesture that sends milk flying for yards. During this time of trial and error, arrange things so that the feeding area will require a minimum of cleaning up after meals. Lay out newspapers in the center of the kitchen floor and place his chair on them. After the meal, you can roll up the papers and throw them away. Put just a little milk in his cup at a time, refilling it as it disappears. Later, when he deliberately spills the milk just for the fun of it, shake your head and let him know by the tone of your voice that this should not be done. If he continues to spill his milk, don't give him any more—he will soon learn that he'd better drink it when he has it.

As Appetite Declines

When he is still in the learner stage, he will expend a lot of energy learning to feed himself and may tire before the meal is over. In this case, don't hesitate to help by feeding him. At the same time, never try to make him eat any more than he wants. It is normal for his appetite to lessen now, as his growth is slowing up. (This isn't true of all babies, however. A few of the little gourmands stow away so much food that you begin to wonder if the budget can stand it!) It is well to be aware that a diminishing appetite often occurs about the time the baby takes over the management of his own meals. He may fiddle around with his spoon and fingers for a little while and then lose interest after consuming an infinitesimal amount of food, but when you try to help by feeding him he definitely doesn't want any more. Remove his plate, and from now on don't give him such large helpings. If he cleans up all you give him, then offer him a little more until he is satisfied.

For a while, he may eat a large breakfast, practically no lunch, and a fair-sized supper; or perhaps lunch will be the big meal, with little eaten at the other meals. It makes no difference. If he is healthy and well adjusted, he will eat all the food his body needs. Many feeding problems start when a mother makes an issue of giving additional food to her baby after he feels he has had enough. Even if she lets him eat lightly at mealtime, she sometimes gives him crackers or cookies between meals. This is a mistake—as you will readily see if you think about it—because the baby stuffed on crackers will not be very hungry at lunchtime, but by 3:00 o'clock he will eat enough crackers again to spoil his supper. Before you know it, your formerly well-trained baby has backtracked to a six-meal-a-day schedule. And he will be eating far too many starches in relation to the meat, fruits, and vegetables he is getting.

Habits that Worry Parents

It is only natural that, as a baby's powers increase and he is able to explore the parts of his own body, he will encounter the genital area and the pleasurable feelings that come when he handles it. This is entirely normal. Perhaps when you change your baby's diaper, or have him stripped for exercise or a sun bath, you will see his hands straying toward this part of his anatomy.

This is nothing to be alarmed about. Don't call attention to what the child is doing, and don't feel anxious. You can distract him by handing him something to play with, but otherwise be unconcerned. Some babies perform a kind of masturbation by rubbing their thighs together. As long as the sex organs are kept clean and healthy, this also can be ignored. Any inflammation of the area should be called to the doctor's attention.

A number of babies around this age begin other practices that cause parents to wonder if they have an abnormal situation on their hands. It is not uncommon for a child of this age to bang his head hard against a wall or the side of the crib, or to roll his head about. Others rock themselves vigorously back and forth on hands and knees, propelling their beds clear across a room.

No one is sure what causes these forms of activity, but they are not a sign of low mentality, as some persons have supposed. The baby is not likely to injure himself with his head banging, but you can pad the side of his crib if it hurts *your* feelings. The habitual rocker is likely to shake his bed to pieces at intervals, but you can tighten the bolts. And if the banging of the crib against the wall annoys you, you can pad the outside of the bed to deaden the sound. These are all manifestations that pass in due time, and no child ever appears to have been the worse for going through them.

Standing

Another use of the play pen is apparent when the baby uses the rungs to pull himself up. That is always a thrilling accomplishment, and we hope that your baby tries it for the first time in the late afternoon so that his father is there to see him. After several minutes of applause on your part and triumphant crowing on Baby's, you may notice that his knuckles are getting white as he hangs on to the pen and that his expression is no longer happy. He has just realized that he doesn't know how to sit down.

If this happens, help him, showing him how to let himself down easily. Almost immediately, up he pops again. And once more he is unable to take the downward plunge. This sequence may continue for several days, and you will neglect your housework because of the time involved in returning the baby to the floor. But the happy day does come when your offspring accidentally lets go, falls down, discovers it doesn't hurt, and from then on spends many happy hours pulling himself up and falling down again.

Protecting Household Treasures

After your little fellow acquires the ability to pull himself up expertly to tables and other surfaces, you enter upon a new stage of existence. This may not occur until somewhere in the second year, but so many babies are a menace to ash trays and such by the end of the first year that you had better prepare for it now.

There are two schools of thought as to the way to meet the new situation. Some authorities say that a yearling cannot be taught to leave things alone, and that the solution is to put everything breakable beyond his reach for a year or more. Others contend that a child big enough to pull himself up is also big enough to learn what he may and may not touch. The writer has reared a child according to each method, and I should like to put in a strong vote for the second school of thought, as opposed to the first.

He Likes to Be Shown

You cannot, of course, *tell* a child of a year or so to leave things alone and expect results. But you can show him in a loving, friendly way what he may and may not handle. The course we followed with Laurie after she had achieved locomotion was to keep her in her play pen except for periods when we could be with her constantly. Wherever we had a pile of magazines or a shelf of books,

we put a few magazines or books that Laurie could have and removed anything that might hurt her or that was fragile. Then we let her out to roam and explore. When she picked up something, we let her examine it, then explained that "This is Mommy's or Daddy's," returned it to its place, and gave her a toy, explaining, "This is Laurie's." When she reached for a book or magazine, we gave her one of hers, repeating the formula. It took patience—you have to be most careful to keep this a happy learning situation—but by the end of about a week, Laurie had grasped the point. From then on we could let her have the freedom of the house without worrying about our belongings.

When Debbie, our second daughter, reached this point, Mommy was ill and Daddy was far away. She was therefore turned loose upon an unsuspecting world without training. Putting things above her reach at home was all right—when one remembered to do it—but taking her to anyone else's house was an ordeal for all concerned. Also, when we had guests, it was a little inconvenient to have to keep ash trays, plates, cups, and glasses on mantels and the tops of bookcases. There are times when one likes to be able to use one's tables. Moreover, we found to our sorrow that it is much harder to teach the lesson of mine and thine after a child has acquired the idea that anything within reach is fair game.

It makes life much simpler to devote a week or two at the beginning of the period of free locomotion to the kind of training Laurie had. Many other parents have followed this system successfully and were glad they took the time to do it.

Even after a child is pretty well trained to leave other people's things alone, he will sometimes pick them up. Ask him politely to put the object back and show him how to do it. By teaching him in this way, you teach him how to handle carefully anything that finds its way into his hands.

Let Him Be Rough Sometimes

While it is possible, and highly desirable, for a child to learn respect for family possessions, he should also have things of his own that he can tear and pound and pummel to his heart's content. Don't give your baby lovely, delicate dolls at first; give a hardy doll that he can chew and throw around as the impulse seizes him. Also, if he has an educational toy, don't insist that he use his in the way it was intended. Certainly you can show him the correct way, but if he finds a different method of playing with it that is more fascinating to him, let him play as he pleases. His books should be made of cloth so that they are untearable, and he should have a few old magazines to rip up.

The child of this age needs to climb. Although he should still spend some time outside in his play pen, he will want to play on the grass, too, and should have a fenced-in outdoor area. Furnish him with something to climb on—large blocks made of light wood are excellent, or anything else you can think of. A sand pile will keep

ing! High-school or college students should be able to bring their books and spend the evening studying; a girl who is to stay until late at night might bring one friend with her. And of course you will always see that a girl gets home safely. But baby sitting is a serious, responsible job and should be viewed in that light by both employer and employee.

Bowel Training

If you have (and wisely) ignored any attempt at bowel training heretofore, you may have some slight success at this time. But even at this stage in the baby's development, it will be just movement catching and not training and can just as well be omitted. If you try it a few times and the baby resists, it is much better to drop the idea and wait until the baby himself wants to start using the toilet. We discuss this more thoroughly on page 160.

Accomplishments

Much of this chapter has been devoted to the accomplishments your baby develops at this age. Don't push him to try any of these things; just help him when he shows himself ready.

Equipment You'll Find Handy Now

Toilet seat. If you should decide to put your baby on the toilet once a day or so, hoping he will have a bowel movement, you will need a comfortable seat for him. Usually the most convenient is a special seat that clamps on the regular toilet. It should have arms, a back rest, a strap in front so the baby feels secure, and a footrest. If your baby is a boy, you will need a deflector—a device that clamps on the front of the seat and deflects the stream of urine. Sometimes it is more convenient to have a nursery chair than a toilet seat. This is a chair with a hole in the seat and a potty that sits under the hole. If your only bathroom is upstairs, a nursery chair on the first floor saves many steps. Many babies just beginning their toilet training feel more secure on an on-the-floor nursery chair than on a seat that fits on the regular toilet. Since we believe in waiting till the baby is capable of some self-help in toileting, he will need either a nursery chair or a sturdy step-stool for climbing onto his toilet seat.

Table and chair. Now that your baby is sitting up you will want a chair for him. Consider your space problems carefully before you buy anything. A table with a seat in the middle is convenient. In it the baby is safe—he is strapped in. He has a table surface in front of him for playing or eating. His seat rocks, which gives him joy. Most of these devices have legs that can be adjusted higher as the baby grows. In addition, some of them are convertible into regular tables when the baby no longer needs to be strapped into the center of his table.

A high chair should have widespread legs to avoid tipping over, and an adjustable foot rest. Use a safety belt or harness to keep Baby from falling. High chairs come in many types—some converting into a junior chair and then into a regular utility chair for adult use.

A stroller. If you don't have a convertible carriage you will need a stroller. Get one that is sturdy and gives good support to the baby's back. Make sure that the baby can be strapped in securely.

CHAPTER TEN

Twelve to eighteen months

Although you still have a cuddly, bouncy baby, at this age you catch a glimmer every now and then of a little boy or girl. One minute you are surprised at an infantile act; the next minute you are equally amazed by a more mature expression or action. He isn't getting much bigger now, but his intelligence is growing by leaps and bounds. Your baby will be a definite little individual by the time he is eighteen months old.

Before we discuss your baby's current skills, let's look at his schedule. Since we don't know what time your particular family rises and shines, we will base our schedule on a 7:00 A.M. start. As usual, you will make your own adaptation.

Suggestions for Handling His Day

Since the baby is eating the same breakfast that you and your husband enjoy, it is convenient for the entire family to breakfast together. After you change his diapers, place the baby in his chair with a cup of milk to sustain him while you pour fruit juice and serve the cereal. The baby can have his juice now, if you like, but to save it for 9:30 or 10:00 makes a nice break in the morning.

As he eats his cereal, you can be making coffee and cooking eggs. Your husband is probably manning the toaster. The baby may tire of the same old soft-boiled egg and appreciate a poached or scrambled egg for a change. Don't give him fried eggs yet—the grease

is too hard for him to digest. If he is not enthusiastic about cereal, make sure that his toast is made from enriched white or whole-grain bread. Should he for some reason not be eating buttered toast, give him milk toast or poached egg on well-cut-up toast.

Morning Nap

After breakfast, try putting the yearling back to bed for at least a half hour. A little nap at this time rests him for a good morning's play. Otherwise, he is likely to become sleepy about 10:30, take his nap then, and sleep until 1:00 or so in the afternoon, becoming very tired and fussy late in the afternoon but refusing to take another nap. During this stage of development, the baby's napping needs are changing, and he may go through several periods when he doesn't seem to know just when he does want to sleep. It is difficult for Mother, but about all you can do is keep the rest of his schedule as regular as possible and give him a few strong hints as to when you think he should sleep.

Ready to Play

At about 9:00 A.M., or whenever you get the baby up from his nap, give him his juice and vitamins and a cracker, and put him outdoors in his play pen. If it is raining, put the pen on the porch, if you have one; otherwise, it will have to be in the house. Let him stay in it as long as he is contented, then release him to play in the fenced-in yard or in his playroom until lunchtime. If he gets fussy before lunch, give him some of his milk, unless this proves to be an appetite spoiler, in which case orange or tomato juice will fill the bill. Perhaps you can plant him in an out-of-the-way corner of the kitchen, giving him your double boiler and one or two clothespins to play with while you work nearby. Babies are usually fascinated with Mother's pots and pans, fitting one inside the other and pulling lids on and off.

Lunchtime

He probably will want his lunch sometime between 11:00 and 12:00. This should consist of a fruit, a vegetable, a starch (potato, rice, macaroni), meat, and milk. If he isn't eating much lunch and has more appetite for supper, switch these meals; give him his heavier meal at night.

Long Nap—We Hope

When he has finished eating, clean him up a bit and tuck him in bed for what we hope will be a long nap.

When you get him up again, offer him a liquid (milk, water, or juice) and a graham cracker and put him once more in his play pen, taking him out when he shows he is tired of it. He can then play by himself in the fenced-in yard until you come out to play with him. When Daddy comes home, perhaps he will want to take charge of the baby.

An Idea for Dad

Sometimes after a hard working day, Daddy feels that the last thing on earth he wants to do is romp with an energetic runabout. What he yearns for is a half hour's nap. Here is a hint for Father. It is possible for you to do both—to rest, yet be with your youngster. Lie on the bed or the living-room rug (on your stomach, preferably) and let the baby crawl over you. He will love it. When his attention flags, all you need to do is wiggle a foot or make an interesting noise and he will immediately be back to the attack. When you find the strength to get up, announce to your child that it is

bathtime and transfer the scene of operations to the bathtub. If your house is equipped with a shower, why don't you and your son bathe together? Take it easy the first few times until the baby is used to the new idea of shower sprays; in fact, if he can watch you take a shower once or twice beforehand, the idea won't be so new and frightening.

Fun in the Water

If it's a tub bath, fill the tub with four or five inches of warm water, wash your child quickly, and then let him play. He still is too young to be left alone in the bathtub even for a minute. If something outside the bathroom demands your attention, either wait until your wife can watch him or wrap a large bath towel around the baby and take him along.

There are two reasons why bathtime is now switched to the evening. The first one is obvious when you look at your grimy offspring; the other is that being in water relaxes and rests the youngster, putting him in the best kind of mood for his supper.

Supper Management

After the bath, the baby will be ready to eat a supper of fruit and/or vegetable, a filling food, perhaps a dessert, and milk. If he didn't have an egg for breakfast, give him one now. It's all right for him to have two eggs a day if he wants one at both meals. If he doesn't have an egg, he will need one filling food. If he tires of cereal, try dressing it up with fruit, brown sugar or honey on top. Or try him on various kinds of sandwiches.

From now on he will be eating more and more of the same things the rest of the family eats, so you will gradually eliminate the canned baby foods. It has generally been found best for babies to eat before their parents do, but if you like an early dinner and the baby isn't diverted from his food by your company, you can eat together. Once his dinner is safely out of the way, he can join you with a piece of zwieback or a plain cookie. Don't make the mistake of letting him beg bits from your plate. It may seem cute at first, but later it be-

comes annoying and you will be unable to eat your dinner in peace. If your child wants more food, fix him a little plate of his own from the things on the family table.

Bedtime Signals

Supper always gives the toddler or runabout a new lease on life, and he will tear through the house, being a most charming and stimulating companion. But all of a sudden it is bedtime. Different children reveal this in different ways. One simply yawns and acts sleepy. Another gets fussy and seems to hurt himself whenever he turns around. A third begins to be too excited and high-strung, doing mischievous little things he knows he shouldn't, like overturning ash trays. Try to catch him before any of this happens, hold him quietly for a few minutes while you sing to him, and then tuck him into bed.

It is best for parents to take turns putting the baby to bed. We heard of a family in which the father invariably took his daughter up to bed. That was fine and everybody was satisfied with the arrangement until one day the father had to leave town on business.

His daughter refused to go to bed and screamed until midnight before she cried herself to sleep. To a child, ritual is ritual. It is best to vary it before it becomes too well established. Besides, parents should share the privilege of bedding down the baby because there is something very special about this privilege. No matter how impish and energetic a baby is during the day, when you are holding him in your arms in his darkened bedroom he becomes somehow a little angel.

Play Arrangements

The baby should have a satisfactory place to play outdoors and in the house, both places calling for a minimum of supervision on the part of his mother.

If you have a large enough house, make a playroom of one room where the baby's indoor toys can be kept and where there is nothing he can't play with. A gate or other barrier through which he can see may be placed across the doorway, keeping him inside but not making him feel as if he were completely shut away. This room

can be equipped with various things to amuse him: steady and sturdy things to climb on; simple wooden toys to pull around on a string; a baby-sized chair (the musical rockers are wonderful and last for years); a drum to bang on (or a pot or pan); mallet-and-peg toy; blocks; cloth books and old magazines; dolls; push-and-pull toys; washable cloth animals; and anything else with which the baby enjoys playing.

Putting Away Can Be Fun

There should be low shelves and a big box where all his toys are kept when not in use, and at the end of the day you and the baby will put things away. You make a game of this—after all, it *can* be fun. At first, you will do all the work, the baby undoing it almost as fast. You have to work swiftly repeating, "Put it back, put it back, put it back," and when the last toy is on the shelf, grab up the baby and quickly take him from the room. After a few days, or even weeks, one evening the baby will get the idea and put a toy on the shelf. Praise him. He will be so thrilled that he will immediately remove the same toy so that he can put it back and be praised again. But have hope, for soon he will be actively helping you and will know what "Put it back" means.

Improved Play Space

If you haven't a playroom—and most families haven't these days—block off a large enough portion of a room to give the run-about sufficient space to range about a bit. You can hide his toy box behind a chair and cover it with a square of attractive material at the end of the day. You will find this play space quite necessary, as the baby can't remain in his pen all day, nor can you spend all your time watching to see that he doesn't get into mischief.

For outdoor play, we should like to stress again the desirability of a fenced-in portion of yard near a tree or some other object furnishing shade. Of course all children need sunshine, but during the hot summer there should be shaded areas where they can play. The different kinds of equipment for the play yard are innumerable: sandbox with bucket and shovel, blocks to climb on, wheeled toys,

a swing with a safety seat, play garden tools, a small wheelbarrow or wagon. Families who have animal pets are lucky, because a friendly dog or cat or perhaps a rabbit in the play yard with Junior keeps him occupied much longer than inanimate toys.

Walking and Talking

Many babies start walking and talking at this age, some a month or two earlier. No matter how many parents tell you that *their* children were walking and talking at a much earlier age than yours, don't let it upset you. It is bad for a baby physically and emotionally to be pushed into anything. Walking and talking early is no indication of high intelligence, nor is slowness in these accomplishments a sign of stupidity. Once upon a time—and this is a true story—

there were twins. Twin A was an unusually precocious baby and the joy of his parents, grandparents, uncles, and aunts. Twin B sat like a bump on a log (once he had mastered sitting, which was a struggle in itself) and didn't even *try* to stand up or talk or play patty-cake. Needless to say, Twin B was a great source of worry to his family. But now those twins have grown up, and both are so alert and intelligent that you would never dream they had had such a different start.

It is in your power to help your child master his new skills, after he has clearly shown an eagerness to learn. When he calls your attention to some object, pronounce its name several times. At first, his imitation of the word may have no relationship to the actual sounds, but gradually it will take on a similarity. Some people seem to be born with an ear for sound, and enunciate well from the first. For others, it is a long-drawn-out process, requiring much practice. Your child may have an instinctive talent for mimicry, in which case he will pick up words quickly without much prompting. Or he may not have the faintest idea how to distinguish between an "ah" or "oh" or "oo." If the latter is true, and he really seems to want to speak English, you might institute a little game in which you take turns mimicking sounds the other makes. Be sure to keep it a game, however, never showing disappointment when Junior's efforts are unintelligible and always stopping when he shows signs of being bored.

The Child Who Is Slow to Talk

Then there are those rugged individuals who, although normal in other phases of development, don't talk until they are close to three years old. Talking, from their standpoint, is an unnecessary bother; why should they talk when they can get what they want by sign language? This is more often true of a baby who has an older brother or sister. The older child often knows what the baby wants and translates to the parents. But before you take it for granted that your baby is just being lazy about talking, you should look into the possibility of his having a hearing deficiency. This is often difficult to detect in a baby, but if you suspect anything of the sort it should be brought to the attention of your doctor immediately. The sooner a deaf child is treated, the better the chance of developing his full hearing powers.

The main thing to remember about talking is that repetition is the keynote. Don't make an issue of it, but neither should you become exasperated if your baby asks you for the fiftieth time, "What's that?" when you have reason to believe that he knows it's a ball. Only by hearing you say words many times will he be able to form the syllables perfectly.

Different Approaches to Walking

The personality of a baby is often expressed by his attitude toward walking. Some approach it cautiously and painstakingly by holding on to furniture for months; then when they feel they have become adept at that, they lengthen their horizon by taking two free steps between closely placed chairs. Some are reckless and overconfident; they don't bother with intermediate practice, but all at once head out for the great open spaces. Invariably babies in this last category fall flat on their faces. This may be enough to convince one baby he isn't ready to walk for several months yet, but another regards it as even more of a challenge and perseveres until he succeeds.

Pleasant as it is to hold a baby in our arms, we all look forward to the day when he can walk. Even the strongest of fathers begin to stagger under the weight of a yearling after they have been carrying him for fifteen minutes. So there is some tendency to urge a baby to walk. But you must remember that two things can result from his walking before he is entirely ready to do so: his muscles may be overtaxed and he may rebel. He knows better than his parents do when the time has come for this accomplishment.

Factors that May Interfere with Walking

Another factor enters into walking, as into every stage of a youn ster's growth. Any change in routine, such as moving or a trip, will often retard development. Perhaps he was already taking a few steps, but after the upheaval in his life took place, he retrogressed completely to crawling. Just be patient. Give him time. After he has made a good adjustment to the new situation, he will be able to carry on with his former skills and add new ones.

Usually They Love It

The average baby, however, is thrilled with the idea of walking and loves to hang on to two adults' hands for balance and security. We can't say that you must leave it to the baby to decide how much of this type of help he wants, or you would probably end up by walking him twenty-four hours a day. You will probably be happiest if you fit walking into his schedule at a regular hour—during the time of day reserved for family playtime, for example. Then the parents can relieve each other. When the baby has reached the point where he tries to take a few faltering steps all by himself, Mother and Father can place themselves a few feet apart and the baby can walk back and forth from one safe pair of arms to the other. He may glory in this new role to such an extent that he will take several extra spills, just for laughs.

As soon as he begins to try to walk, he should have a pair of good walking shoes. A certain baby who dallied with walking for months but never could bring herself to step out alone, was presented with a pair of shoes. When she stood up in them, she began to walk. Your doctor will either prescribe shoes for your baby or will recommend a store where the salespeople are expert at fitting small children.

CHAPTER ELEVEN

What kind of discipline?

Ever since the rearing of children became a subject of scientific inquiry, discipline has been a controversial point. To some persons—perhaps too many—it is a word spoken with grim visage and set lips. It carries connotations of punishment—spankings and scoldings, sitting in the corner, and going to bed without supper.

Many people still believe firmly that children will be ruined unless early in life they meet with some one of the foregoing kinds of unpleasantness. Their only question is what form of unpleasantness is the most effective.

Some people believe just as firmly that punishments or regulation of any kind are archaic. Let children grow according to their natural bent, they say, without interference, and all will work out in time.

Oddly enough, the results of both of these theories, in the hands of some parents, can be much the same. Most delinquents prove to have had enough beatings to turn them into angels, if that were the way to produce angels. And psychiatrists now tell us that children reared with no discipline and no curbing may be as insecure and unhappy, and even delinquent, as those too much punished.

Perhaps the question of discipline has been largely an academic one with you up to the present time. Certainly only a sadist or an utterly nonunderstanding person would punish a baby! But as your child develops powers of locomotion, along with ideas of

his own, sooner or later some of his ideas are bound to clash with yours. When this happens, what is the best thing to do, from the point of view of your youngster's future well-being?

What Discipline Is

First of all, let us look at the word "discipline," discarding our emotional prejudices about it—and it *is* a word about which people are inclined to be very emotional indeed. It does not mean punishment. It comes from the same Latin word that produced "disciple," meaning a learner or follower. The one who does the discplining, therefore, should think of himself as a teacher and guide.

When we approach the subject of discipline in the true meaning of the word, we realize that it is fundamentally a matter of giving direction where direction is needed.

Children come into this world not knowing how to meet and get along in its "booming confusion." It takes many years to learn all the different kinds of behavior required in a civilization as complex as ours. There are things a child may do—and things he may not do which seem very similar to him. It is long before he can understand why some activities are approved while equally delightful ones are frowned upon.

There are certain commands he must obey instantly, for safety's sake. Yet it is important for him to develop initiative and independence in order, eventually, to deal with many situations himself. We want him to learn to curb unwise impulses, to think before he acts, but we don't want to make a child unduly cautious and timorous. It is our responsibility to see that he develops a code of right and wrong, without at the same time building feelings of shame and guilt that will haunt him the rest of his life.

He Wants to Learn

All this is not as difficult as it may sound, for every child wants to learn. There is no such thing as an innately "bad" child. "Bad" children have been badly guided, or neglected in some vital way. Scolding a child, or punishing him for things he didn't mean to do or which it is natural that he should do at his age, is likely to lead to rebellion. He learns nothing constructive from this kind of discipline. He is more likely to feel he is unloved.

To be sure, if a child is certain of his parents' love, he will make allowances for them even if they punish him severely. Our children need our love so much that they desperately want to believe in us—even forgive us! But when we love our children deeply and understandingly, we are not apt to treat them unjustly. A great many parents have found that they can rear fine, responsible, well-disciplined children without nagging and spanking. Such discipline is based, first of all, on an understanding of child growth and development. It also requires self-understanding and self-discipline on the part of the parents.

Regularity the Basis of Discipline

We have mentioned before the part that reasonable regularity of schedule plays in the child's health and sense of well-being. Regularity might be described as the framework of discipline—for parents as well as for children—and it is as important for toddlers and preschoolers as it is for infants. Occasional variations may be unavoidable. But you will generally find that it is on the days when meals are late, or the nap skipped, or bedtime postponed, that Junior is most trying. Should Junior be punished if this is the case? Isn't it more intelligent, as well as fairer, to try to keep to the schedule in which Junior is able to be his best self? Where household operations flow smoothly, not in a tense, worried way, with the homemaker planning ahead and arranging her day, incidents of "naughtiness" are much less frequent than in helter-skelter, hurried, worried homes, where a child doesn't know what will happen next. This doesn't mean a return to the overroutinized, sternly efficient regime that a good many women have known in offices before marriage. Rather, it means a simplified schedule for the mother, so that the necessary things get done without too much strain. For the child it means that he feels secure because his world is an orderly one. His meals come along on time. Most days follow a regular pattern of play, naps, and rides, Daddy's home-coming, and the bed routine. The pattern is flexible, to be sure, but there is a pattern and the child enjoys it. He likes to feel that he knows what will happen next in his small world.

Play Arrangements Important

We have mentioned play arrangements which will allow the child to do his own playing and experimenting without coming into conflict with adult affairs. This is another very important point. As children get older they have need for larger spaces where they can run and shout and quarrel and explore with a minimum of interference. This, again, is a great preventer of so-called "behavior problems." We might say that a home which furnishes these two requisites —reasonable orderliness and proper arrangements for children's play—

is the setting which will make it easiest for your child to develop well and happily. But the determining factor is the attitude toward the child of the important people in his life—Father and Mother.

Learn How He Grows

The first requisite here is to understand how a child grows and what behavior to expect at each stage of growth. Right now you are probably observing one of the most moving things we know of—the long, slow struggle a baby goes through to become expert in walking. You have witnessed the urge that impelled your little fellow to take his first staggering, uncertain steps. You have witnessed, too, the many obstacles he must overcome before he can run about freely. His legs and body muscles must grow strong, he must attain a sense of balance, he must plunge headlong on his face time and time again. Sometimes he strikes out in determined and reckless forays. Sometimes he gets scared, and goes back to creeping, or insists on an adult finger to cling to.

We don't think of punishing a toddler because he doesn't walk like a grownup at his first attempt. But there is an inclination to expect perfection when it comes to behavior. It is only recently that we have come to realize that mental, emotional, and social growth proceed in the same slow way that prowess in walking does—with many initial failures, with countless setbacks—before a child can master the new techniques and make them his own. A whole host of things in the past have been considered problems which were not problems at all but only the natural way of a small being trying with the utmost earnestness to adapt himself to his environment or to learn new skills. The sad thing is that so many parents have made problems, where none have existed at all, by their ignorance of these fundamental facts.

Thumb-sucking Bogey

It may be said, therefore, that one of the greatest contributions of science during the past generation has been to remove sources of needless parental worry and conflict with the children they love. To name just one instance: thirty years ago there was a great hue and cry about thumb-sucking, which we mentioned in an early chapter. Conscientious parents were plunged into consternation when they saw their infant put his thumb in his mouth. Weird, bizarre methods were used to circumvent him, usually with the result that the baby sucked more determinedly. Then science discovered that sucking is an inborn need of the infant, and that babies will stop thumb-sucking of their own accord—if it hasn't been made a source of conflict—when the purpose it serves in their development is achieved.

As science has delved more and more deeply into child nature, more and more of these natural laws of growth have come to light. We know that there are certain periods when a formerly well-behaved child becomes willful, stubborn, contrary. Or at least he seems that way. But what is happening is that he is trying to become independent. Just as an inner urge set the baby on his feet and made him attempt to walk, whether he could or not, so at later stages a child feels impelled to break loose from domination and try things on his own. The first of these periods is not far ahead—we'll talk about it in the chapter on the child of two or three, page 154. A second often occurs when a youngster starts to school, and a third, in some ways the most spectacular of all, when he enters adolescence.

Sign to Give More Freedom

Parental understanding of what is going on will not automatically do away with a child's willful behavior in these periods. But parents who know that their child has come to a new stage in his development are much better able to guide him wisely toward it than are the ones who look upon the behavior as wholly reprehensible, to be squelched forthwith. The former invariably find that when their youngster is allowed more freedom in things he can handle, he will be more willing to accept the restrictions that must still be imposed for his own good.

We know that there will be periods of clinging closely to Mother, when the whole business of growth suddenly seems overwhelming to the young adventurer. There are likely to be periods of fear, sometimes springing from an outward cause, sometimes rising out of the child's inner bewilderment and confusion. To shame a child or try to talk him out of such behavior does no good and is more likely to intensify it. But if parents supply a little extra love and reassurance, the child can be counted upon to grow out of the clinging and the fears in the course of time.

Pretty soon now, your child will be undertaking details of his physical care—dressing and undressing, feeding himself, attending to toilet needs. You will see how very long it takes to master the technique, so simple to us, of slipping a button through a buttonhole. It is well to remember that learning the techniques of human relationships is an even longer and more bewildering process for the child. His impulse is to grab, or to defend himself against aggression by any handy weapon. He bites, pulls hair, kicks, and screams. This does not mean that he is going to be a nonsocial being when he grows up.

When to Step In

Parents may protect a youngster against bullying aggression that is too much for him to handle. They may divert his attention to other things when he wants to seize all the toys for himself, and explain that other people have rights, too. But there is no need to worry about the seemingly antisocial behavior displayed when small children are taking their first steps toward association with their fellows.

One of the most interesting, and in some ways most valuable, new contributions in the field of child development is a better understanding of the hostile and angry feelings children express. There will be times when they will declare they hate their own parents. Formerly, this was considered a very shocking thing, meriting severe punishment. Parental energies were directed toward suppressing temper and hostility.

Let Angry Feelings Show

The modern attitude is to let these angry feelings come out in the open, accept them calmly, and thus let the child free himself of his burden of antagonism and rebellion. Psychiatrists tell us that the hostile feelings we were required to throttle down in childhood continue to churn about in the subconscious, and are the reason for the hateful actions of which we are so much aware in the adult world.

This does not mean that we shall sit back calmly and let the child do himself and others harm or do everything he feels like. But we should understand rage as a sign of inner conflict or of frustration. Perhaps the child has worked long and earnestly to build a house of blocks but is defeated by a too ambitious plan. He is angry and cries. Parents can become wise in learning when it is time to step in with a little help—but not too much help—and when it is time to

turn the child's attention to some other undertaking. The mother who lets her angry child bang his blocks about and work out his rage in that way is wise—provided he does no harm. Children who can express their anger and know that they will be loved and accepted just the same, and that their parents will give complaints a fair hearing, gradually learn to control their violent emotions.

Reverting to Baby Ways

We may anticipate that when a small child's world is thrown out of kilter, he is apt to regress to more infantile behavior. This often happens when a new baby is born, or if a mother has to go to the hospital, or if the child is placed in strange surroundings. Bed-wetting, temper tantrums, or thumb sucking under such circumstances are likely to be the rule rather than the exception. Children who have been made uncertain of their status are helped by reassurance, not punishment. When they are confident that they are safe and still loved as before, they will abandon the infantile behavior.

If parents are at odds with each other, children invariably feel the strain and tension in the atmosphere. In a divided home, a youngster will learn at an early age to play one parent off against the other. Or the child who does not get the parental love and care that he needs may resort to annoying behavior, since this is the only way he knows to call attention to himself.

Agree on a Plan

Parents should agree on the plan they will follow with their youngster. Nothing is more confusing to the small child than to be punished by one parent and indulged by the other for the same form of behavior. When children react as we would like them to do, we should be generous with our praise and make as little fuss as we can about types of behavior we don't like. Children need to feel important. When they can get parental approval and commendation by being "good," that is the way they will want to be. On the other hand, they should not be made to feel unloved because they are "bad." Accept occasional trying behavior and don't make too much fuss about it. None of us is perfect every minute!

Prepare Him When You Can

Many a conflict can be forestalled by preparing a child in advance for the advent of another baby into the family. We discuss this in Chapter Thirteen. It works just as well in incidents of everyday life. Three-and-a-half-year-old Laurie and I, to give adult guests a breathing spell on Sunday, are walking down to the river. It occurs to me that this may create a situation, inasmuch as Laurie's accustomed sport at the river is throwing stones into the water. That is a grubby pursuit, and today she is dressed in her best.

So I explain that today we will just sit and watch the river, because the rocks are sooty from the passing trains, and Laurie's dress is too pretty to soil. Tomorrow she can wear her old clothes and throw stones in the water to her heart's content.

Laurie sits quietly on the bank, watching the boats and trains go by. As we walk back up the hill, she chants, "I said I wouldn't throw any stones, and I didn't throw a single stone. We throw stones when we have our old clothes on." Laurie is proud and happy in having met a new situation that had been explained fairly and reasonably beforehand.

Children adore being taken behind the scenes of adult decision. Your youngster may surprise you by the graciousness of the concessions he is willing to make.

Puzzling Moments

Sometimes, of course, it is difficult to know whether behavior is a result of a new growth urge or a symptom of an undesirable trend. But when you have a generally happy, reasonable, amenable youngster, it does no harm to wait a bit and see. If something has happened in your youngster's life that could well account for the behavior—such as one of the sudden changes we have mentioned, or too much excitement—we can certainly give the effects a chance to wear off before becoming alarmed. If rebellion occurs at a period when most children are rebellious, it is better to take it in stride, trusting to natural growth and development to take care of it. If a child is ill, we can afford to wait until he is well again. And of course, if the behavior wears off, we know that there was no need to worry.

If his upsetting behavior continues far past the time when it should be left behind, or if one kind of obstreperousness is simply replaced by another, try to get some expert advice.

What About Disobedience?

The best child in the world will be disobedient at times. What do you do in such a case? It may be that you are asking more than should be expected at his stage of development. If so, the matter should not be pressed. But if you have asked him to do something you feel is necessary for his own good, take him by the hand in a firm but friendly way and see that he does it.

Sometimes the usually happy, amenable child who becomes suddenly rebellious is coming down with an illness. Try giving him a rest with a picture book or other quiet pastime. You will soon know whether he was letting off emotional steam or whether he is ill.

A child wants to win his parents' approval. When you make

allowances for the inadequacies that are part of being a child, and show appreciation of the efforts he puts forth, you will find him cooperating to the extent of his powers. When he knows you are on his side, he will usually want to do what you ask.

Wait—But Watch Too

The wise parents of old knew that their children would outgrow undesirable ways of behaving. The wise parent today knows that these are a part of growth–and there we have the advantage. We can watch the onward trend that is always taking place, and refuse to be disturbed by the trial-and-error period when a child is thrusting forward to a new, maturer phase. If he is struggling with something beyond his abilities, it may be that we can help. If he gets discouraged, we can show him cheerfully that he has really accomplished quite a lot. If he wants to wait a while before making another attempt, we can be patient. We can show him at all times that we care, that we are interested, and that we know he is going to work it out.

If your child has your love, sympathy, and understanding; if you are ready with a bit of guidance where guidance is needed, but can keep hands off when he is going in the right direction unaided–he will work out his problems.

How a typical one-year-old behaves

Here you see a typical day in the life of a one-year-old, as determined by important scientific study and research.

WAKING

Wakes between 6 and 8 A. M. Generally calls out instead of crying. Happy to see Mother.

Needs changing. Cracker will satisfy immediate hunger.

Can be put back into crib where he will play by himself for half-hour to hour.

BREAKFAST AND DRESSING

Fair appetite for breakfast. Cereal and cup of milk are mainstays. Likes to hold cup himself.

Frequently has an after-breakfast bowel movement. But may resist the potty. Don't force him.

Cooperates in dressing by putting arm in sleeve, holding out leg for pants.

MORNING ACTIVITIES

Likes to climb and cruise, pulling books out of shelves . . .

. . . handling things on low table—so it's wise to keep valuables out of reach.

Asserts himself by saying "No!" even about going out—and other things he really likes.

Enjoys hour in play pen. Likes toys that fit inside each other, clothespins and basket.

Likes to toss things out. May cry when he can't reach them.

Shows readiness for nap by fussing. Nap lasts about two hours. May skip morning nap, then sleep after lunch.

LUNCH

Awakens and is toileted. May show interest in procedure and product.

Appetite generally good but varies, due to teething and other growth factors.

Likes to eat with his fingers. Starting to develop ability to spoon-feed himself.

AFTERNOON

If baby tires of self-feeding, a toy will divert him while Mother finishes the job.

Relishes an afternoon carriage ride. Watches movement of cars and people.

Likes to watch other children playing. But isn't yet ready to play with them.

AND EARLY EVENING

Ready for a period of social activity. Delights in being chased and hiding.

Likes to practice walking with his hand held or in baby walker.

Enjoys playing put-and-take with an adult.

Correctly uses "Mama," "Dada," and a few other words.

Suspicious of strangers at first meeting. Warms up to them gradually if they don't rush him.

Enjoys his bath. Likes to play with washcloth, soap and water toys.

SUPPER AND SLEEP

Cereal and fruit are frequently favored. May want a bottle to take to bed.

May go to sleep right after supper—or walk around crib and play on top of covers first.

CHAPTER TWELVE

Eighteen months to two years

The schedule for the baby of this age is practically the same as the one he has been following. He will probably drop his morning nap, if he hasn't done so already. You may find that if he does take a nap in the morning, he won't sleep in the afternoon, and you may have a very fussy youngster on your hands long before the supper hour. (In this case, it is a good idea to bathe him earlier than usual; it will have a soothing effect on his disposition.) Yet the child of this age may need some rest during the long interval between breakfast and lunch. You might try returning him to his bed for half an hour or so after breakfast, but not leaving him so long that he will fall asleep.

His diet is very similar to that of an adult, but he still mustn't eat richly seasoned or spiced foods or pastries. Nor should he have hot breads.

Eating Phases

Anywhere from twelve months on, throughout the preschool years, your child is apt to go through varied eating phases. For a while he may eat everything in sight. Next thing you know, he may cut down to such a small amount of food that you don't see how he can survive. If he hasn't started this before, he is apt to do so around eighteen months.

Your child may also go on binges of eating one type of food to the exclusion of others. Thus, in one period he may have an enormous appetite for fruit, a small one for other food items. Next, the emphasis may be on meat, or eggs, or some particular vegetable. At times, he may consume prodigious quantities of milk; at other times, he may take only a little.

These variations of eating habits do no harm, provided the child is not permitted to fill up on sweets and starches to the exclusion of the foods containing protein, vitamins, and minerals—those, of course, being meats of various kinds, eggs, cheese, milk, vegetables, and fruits. If starch and sweets are allowed only in amounts sufficient to balance the other foods, most children can be counted on to eat a well-balanced diet over a period of a week or so. Encourage your child to take at least one bite of everything on his plate, but after that you may let him gorge himself on his preference, whether it is for eggs or meat or fruit or vegetables. (We knew a three-year-old who for a while ate four eggs for breakfast every morning—without any bad effects!)

Those "Picky" Times

There may come times when Junior just picks at his food for days at a stretch, and this is trying since there seems to be a rather close connection between good meals and good behavior. If such times drag on, your doctor should be consulted. If the doctor says there is nothing wrong, just be patient and see it through. It may end in a spell of big eating. In the meantime, try, without urging, to tempt your child's appetite by making his food and plate especially attractive.

Many children have an aesthetic sense in regard to the color, texture, and design of food. They like variety, too. On your toddler's plate place one smooth food (such as mashed potatoes, squash, strained fruit); one crunchy food (such as lettuce, thin carrot curls); and one chewy food (chopped meat, diced cooked vegetable, macaroni.) Make each plate colorful. Don't give him potatoes, cabbage, applesauce, and fish at the same meal, because that is a colorless combination. A child is intrigued by the sight of a plate containing red tomato, green spinach, white potato, and meat. Both of you will get a great deal of pleasure—the mother from arranging it, the child from seeing it—when food is interestingly served. For instance, you can put a mound of rice in the center of the plate, thin wedges of tomato going out from it like spokes in a wheel, and in the intermediate spaces alternating dabs of meat and vegetable. And on days when he seems to be eating nothing at all, his appetite might be stimulated if he is the designer of his plate, telling you how he wants the different foods arranged.

Playmates Needed

He is now at an age when he needs the companionship of other children. He is too young for cooperative play, but he likes to be in the same room or the same yard with another child his age. You are fortunate if you live in a neighborhood where there are other children. Several times a week you can arrange alternating visits with the other mothers, and while you chat the youngsters can play. There will be arguments about toys, but don't interfere unless it is necessary. Repeat several times, "We take turns. Jimmy plays with the ball now, and when he is through Johnny can have it." Then leave them alone. Try to keep an eye on them without their being aware of it, because when children know that Mamma is right there they don't behave nearly as well as when they are alone. If Johnny is a bully and Jimmy whimperingly takes everything that is dished out to him, give them several days to work it out. Jimmy, when sufficiently goaded, will probably fight back eventually and so put an end to his martyrdom. Sometimes, however, this doesn't happen and Jimmy shows signs of turning into a permanent Mr. Milquetoast, junior grade. In this case, give him a vacation from Johnny, letting him play with less aggressive children until you feel he has acquired more self-confidence. Do this in such a way, however, that Jimmy doesn't get the idea he has an ever-ready protectress and can run to you to fight his battles for him.

Every child, sooner or later, must learn to give and take. And he has to learn this through association with other children; adults can't teach him. Nor can you expect him to learn this overnight. Your child will be self-centered for several years yet, and he may be a battle-scarred veteran of four or five before he begins to learn how to play cooperatively.

He'll Learn from Companionship

Besides learning give-and-take from children his own age, your youngster will pick up many other things. Upon occasion, a child who has been slow in walking will begin to walk when he sees that another child is an old hand at it. Or he may begin to feed himself, if he hasn't before, by following the example of another child. To be sure, sometimes the opposite is true. The little fellow who has been feeding himself for weeks may decide that since Jimmy Jones gets fed, he might as well get fed, too. It does no harm for his mother to treat this as a joke and feed him a few times—at the same time gently reminding him that he is no baby and can feed himself. If no great fuss is made about it, he will soon go back to his former independence and feed himself.

We hope you won't be the type of parent who says, "Junior, look how well little Sally eats her lunch all by herself. Isn't she a smart little girl?" That is one sure way of making Junior hate little Sally and stubbornly refuse to imitate her. He will also feel that his parents would rather have Sally than him for their child. In bringing up children, it helps to remember Mrs. Malaprop's sage remark, "Comparisons are odorous."

If there are no other children in your neighborhood, arrange visits at least once a week, if possible, to homes where there are small children. Your offspring will be at a social disadvantage if he doesn't know of the existence of other creatures like himself!

He Learns to Talk

If your baby is to learn to speak well, you should talk plainly to him. Don't indulge in baby talk. Pity the poor child who learns English under such a handicap as, "Does him wants him shoozies on?" He won't learn to speak easily, on the other hand, if you toss four-syllable words at him. Use simple language that he can understand, enunciate clearly, and use correct grammar. People who normally speak very rapidly should slow down a bit when talking with young children. Occasional baby talk that slips out naturally won't hurt any child, of course; in fact, he may like it. Certainly we should be natural with our children.

Even the child who speaks extremely well will pronounce a few words in an unorthodox and funny way. Don't imitate him or make fun of him. Save up your laughter for times when the child isn't around and can't overhear you repeating his garbled words. If somebody else imitates the baby, you can say, "We think Junior speaks very well." Then change the subject, and your friend will understand.

There are wide differences in the rate of speech development among normal children. One study of two-year-olds found a range of from five to 1212 words. But around this age, most children begin to make rapid gains in putting words together in phrases and sentences, though some will not acquire all the correct speech sounds for several years. If, however, your baby does not react normally to noises, or if there is decided delay in his speech development, consult a specialist. Corrective treatment for deafness, including use of hearing aids, is now often begun in infancy.

Creative Experiences

Children invariably love music from the time they are only a few months old. They enjoy being sung to, even when the caroling parent can produce at best a dismal monotone. The baby may laugh at your efforts, but he responds to the rhythm all the same and may add his own strange crooning to form a duet. You must not turn the tables and laugh at him; he will be hurt to the quick. Encourage his singing and his swaying, and every night before he is tucked into bed, spend a few minutes singing to him. As he grows older, the time can be longer—perhaps a regular family singing session. If you have a piano, or any musical instrument, and one of you can play—even if with only one finger—that will add to the fun.

A Start in Music

During the day, turn the radio on to musical programs. It is interesting to find that a baby enjoys the very best music, as well as simpler rhythms. A phonograph is an excellent investment for the family. Record companies are turning out charming records for children of all ages. Little tots soon learn the songs by heart as they sing along with the record, and their pitch improves with practice. You will want a sampling of many different kinds of music. Children like variety, and they often make up their own dances to suit different rhythms. It is fun to watch them interpret jazz, semiclassical, and classical compositions. Don't urge them to listen. Just turn on the music. It is a wonderful thing for a child to grow up in a home where there is plenty of music.

Picture Books

Many children of a year enjoy looking at washable cloth picture books, and some will listen to a story by the time they are eighteen months old, though they may understand practically nothing of it. Others are not ready for stories until they are around two and a half, but they will enjoy picture books of their own just the same.

The World of Stories

When youngsters reach an age when they understand stories, all sorts of fascinating storybooks are available. Most of the children's classics, such as *Puss in Boots* and *Mother Goose*, delight this generation just as much as they delighted preceding ones. One of the several compilations of these favorite tales will probably be worn threadbare. But youngsters delight in newer stories, too, and you should add to your child's library from time to time one of the lovely new books that are constantly appearing.

Father and Mother may take turns reading to the child each night when he is ready for bed. If one parent has to read night after night, he may get tired of it—for the child is apt to insist on *The Three Bears* or *The Three Little Pigs* for a month straight. It's more fun for your youngster if you enjoy it, too. Read slowly, and get the full meaning out of the story.

Child Art

During the second year, most children like to play with pencil or crayons and paper. Later, before they are tempted to smear salves and cosmetics on furniture or wallpaper, your move is to furnish them with paints. Poster paints, big sheets of newsprint, and an easel are excellent investments. So are jars of finger paints. Always let the child paint as he pleases. Never show him how, and don't criticize his productions. At first, the child just smears color, with no attempt to produce any particular effect. To him, these works of art are most satisfying. Later, his trees may have red trunks and orange leaves, his men and women very peculiar proportions indeed. But that is the way he wants them to be, and it means a great deal to him to put them down that way.

He's Expressing Something

The young child does not draw or paint in order to produce something beautiful to look at. To him, this is a way to express what he feels and to portray the way things appear to *him*. He has not yet enough command of language to put subtle inner emotions into words, but here is a method of communication that he can employ, if he is allowed to create in his own way. The undirected and untrammeled use of art materials is an important part of his development and is a help to him in working out his problems. As he tries to convey his feelings about objects or experiences by putting them down on paper, he is also learning to understand them better. And the very ability to express himself as he likes is a help toward overcoming troubling emotions. So provide him with art materials and let him express himself with them as he likes.

Inculcating Neatness

We are not asking you to be one of those women who make a fetish of a never-disordered house. We don't feel comfortable around that type of housekeeper ourselves. But we would like to point out that now is the best time in your child's life to incorporate the idea of putting things away after he has finished with them. He should be allowed to strew his things about as he likes during his play periods. And a masterpiece of block building, for instance, may well be left for a time, even in the middle of the living-room floor, so that others may have an opportunity to see and enjoy it. But we would like to stress again the advantages of having the youngster put ordinary toys away at the end of play, as a natural and normal part of his habit patterns.

We have already mentioned the way to start this with indoor playthings—quite lovingly and nonchalantly (see page 100). Now that your youngster is old enough to be spending a good deal of his playtime outdoors, the outdoor things should be put away as well. If your house has no porch or other protected place for storing these toys in bad weather, you can pile them next to the house and cover them with a piece of waterproof canvas. If you do this faithfully every day for some time and then forget about it one night, your youngster will probably remind you. Putting away becomes as much a habit as playing, and is all part of the fun.

Facilities for Self-help

Every child should have facilities for self-help, and when he is about two years of age he may become interested in using them. There should be shelves of drawers in his room low enough for him to reach easily, and low hooks for such things as jackets, pajamas, bathrobe. Whenever he changes his clothes, the adult who is with him should put the articles that are removed neatly back in place, commenting briefly about it. When Junior feels like helping, he will. He may bring everything over to you so that you can put them away, or perhaps you will divide the articles with him and take turns hanging them up.

Good for Parents, Too

Maybe you aren't the neatest person in the world. You will now make a change for the better because you can't very well ask Junior to take care of his things if your room is never in order. Youngsters have been known to make penetrating remarks about their parents' habits of strewing *their* possessions about! He may even bring some of *your* things to you and suggest that you put them away.

Most housewives will tell you that half of their working day is spent picking up around the house. Then, no sooner is the home all cleaned up and neat than various members of the family get it all out of order again. It takes about five minutes for the average family to accomplish this disorder. Few people seem to realize that keeping a house neat and presentable calls for care and responsibility on the part of every family member. Everyone should hang up his own clothes and should clean up his own disorder. But don't have *too high* standards of neatness or order where young children are concerned. A home should be a home, and this means that members of the family should be free to have their possessions about.

A Good Compromise

Often, a livable compromise consists in keeping the living room in good order, since all the family and their guests use it, but allowing a good deal of leeway in the child's room. Even so, shelves for books and toys, a well-equipped closet, and plenty of drawer space should help to make each child's room presentable.

A Word about Manners

Manners are not so much the correct use of the right fork at the right time as they are the expression of courtesy and consideration toward other people. A child becomes courteous and considerate (or otherwise) by imitating the manners of the people around him, and by the way he feels toward persons. If you pounce on him and demand a prettily expressed "thank you" for everything that is done for him, he may be browbeaten into saying the words but he won't be sincerely grateful. Have you ever seen a little child, given a new toy, beam with happiness, then look listless at his parents' reminder, "Now what do you say, Junior? Say 'Thank you' "? Wasn't the smiling face enough? Do we give children things in order to hear them say "thank you," or to make them happy?

On the other hand, there are children who amaze us by producing, at a very early age, "thank you's" that are both voluntary and warm. They like to say it because they have heard their parents do so and because it pleases other people.

Politeness Is "Catching"

If adults are polite to each other and to their children, youngsters acquire the habit of politeness as a natural way of life. When Father makes a practice of pulling out Mother's chair at the table, his young son feels proud when he is allowed to do the same. The rule holds true for many pleasant and courteous ways of behaving, such as thanking a hostess for a good time, opening the door for others, picking up things for older persons, and so on.

Children from homes where there is love and consideration and simple courtesy cannot possibly turn out to be boors. Children are only apt to refuse to be polite when conforming has been made unpleasant by being overstressed, or by the youngster's feeling that the parents are not sincere in their efforts to say and do "the right thing."

Comes a time, somewhere in the teens, when boys and girls yearn to know the usages of polite society, and devour etiquette books if they are available. You can afford to be patient through the intermediate stages.

What to expect of a two-year-old

Here you see a typical day in the life of a two-year-old, based on observations of hundreds—every one different.

Plays happily in crib for half an hour after waking. Glad to see his mother.

Most children are wet in morning, even if they are picked up during night.

Eats small breakfast with some self-feeding.

May want bathroom privacy. Occasional stool smearing. Provide clay, finger paints.

TYPICAL MORNING ACTIVITIES

Interested in dressing and undressing. Can put arms into armholes, feet into pants.

Likes to imitate, help with house, run errands.

If given opportunity, can turn room topsy-turvy.

Uses 3-word sentences. Refers to self by name. Vocabulary grows by leaps and bounds.

Builds tower of 6 or 7 cubes. Likes to play with action toys, trains, toy telephone.

May say "No" to almost every request, occasional temper tantrums.

BEHAVIOR TRAITS

Enjoys playing near another child, but not actually with him.

Grabs other child's toys—refuses to share any of his own.

Likes to help fix lunch and feed himself—still spills a lot. May ask to be fed.

AFTERNOON AND

Usually naps but with some difficulty. May need to be waked up after 2 or 3 hours.

Likes stroller, car rides, walking on curbings and low walls.

Likes rhythmic patterns. Recites short rhymes, sings part of songs, usually off key.

Enjoys painting, clay. Likes to point to and name objects in picture books.

Relishes rough-and-tumble, though best not to overstimulate him before bedtime.

Some children find it hard to be with both parents at once.

Affectionate toward mother. Frequently whines and clings to her.

If mother is pregnant, wise to tell child baby is growing inside her.

Upset if a member of the family is absent for a few days or if family moves.

Both jealous and loving toward new baby. Good to get jealousy out in the open.

Helps wash himself in bath. Intrigued by water play.

Likes to help prepare supper. Feeds self to some extent.

May have second bowel movement after eating. Proud of success, upset by failure.

Often finds it hard to fall asleep. Many demands. May come out of room.

Resists being picked up at night, though girls may wake themselves for toileting.

CHAPTER THIRTEEN

A new baby in the family

It seems to be the style nowadays for young couples to have their babies in groups of two, the second following the first after an interval of about two years. They reason that as long as they are tied down with one baby anyway they may as well be tied down with two. They also feel that children close to each other in age will have more in common and be better companions for each other.

It is quite possible, therefore, that at this stage in the life of the youngster we have been following, he is shortly to be presented with a baby brother or sister.

If that is the case, you, his parents, may be confronted with a kind of worry different from that attending the coming of the first baby. You are no longer timid about caring for a tiny infant. But you have read a great deal about sibling jealousies and about behavior problems in the former only child who is confronted with a rival. You wish to introduce the new baby into the household with a minimum of conflict and heartache on the part of the first-born.

Prepare Him for It

The idea, obviously, should not be sprung on him without loving preparation. And the best preparation of all is to include him as much as possible in the planning, so that he will feel he owns a share in the baby when it appears on the scene. If he is still a baby himself, he won't understand exactly what is going on, but it is a good idea to let him hear Mother and Father discuss the impending event. As each article of furniture and clothing is being made ready, Mother or Father should casually remark that it is for the new baby.

A child between one and two years of age has a sievelike memory. If you tell him months ahead of time that Mother will go away for a few days and have a baby, he will become confused when she never seems to go. To him a month is like a year, and soon the idea will become unreal. But since you mustn't leave him abruptly, start telling him about it two weeks or so before the baby is due. Say

it very simply in one or two sentences, and repeat the same wording as much as possible. You might say something like this: "Mother is going away to a hospital and we will have a new tiny baby. Then she and the baby will come home."

Chance for Sex Education

If the child is older, you can add to this brief information and lay the basis for sex education in a natural, happy way. Answer every one of his questions as truthfully as you can, yet briefly and to the point, but give him only the information he asks for. A simple question such as, "Where do babies come from?" needs the simple answer, "From inside their mothers." In your zeal to be frank and modern, don't make the mistake of taking this opportunity to reveal all the facts of life. A little information at a time, given in a matter-of-fact manner, is what the child wants. This is easier, too, for the parent who is squeamish about discussing sex with his children. By the second or third time that Junior asks the first question, Mother and Father will be rather bored and therefore relaxed in their answers, and questions will seem natural to everyone concerned.

Let Him In on Preparations

By all means, let the older child (probably from age three on) assist in the preparations as much as he likes. He can help arrange the baby's room or corner, he can join in the painting of furniture, he can help put away the baby's clothing. If Mother does any sewing, small daughter or son will love to have a square of cloth, a large needle, and thread, to do "pretend" sewing.

He may be thrilled if you let him place his hand on your abdomen to feel the baby kick. You can tell him that once upon a time he kicked like that. Your attitude of happy anticipation will be contagious.

Your present child will be much more receptive to the new baby if you refer to "our" baby rather than "my" baby. Always include him; never let him feel left out. See if you can find pictures of newborn babies so that your child will know what to expect. He is probably picturing in his mind a pretty, roly-poly playmate of about his own age. When a child is unprepared for the reddish, helpless mite a new baby actually is, he is often shocked and repelled when he sees his baby brother or sister for the first time.

While Mother Is Away

The parents should make careful plans for the first child during the mother's absence. If he has to be away from home, make sure it is with people he knows and likes. If someone is coming to the house to pinch-hit for Mother, have this person come a few days ahead of time, if possible, or at least drop in occasionally to acquaint herself with Junior and his schedule.

The fact of being separated from his mother will be upsetting to the child, even if he doesn't show it openly, so to help him through this period the housekeeper should carefully follow his regular schedule. The child will draw comfort from this. And also a few extra privileges won't be amiss—enough to make him feel he still rates.

Father should spend as much time as possible with his firstborn. To be bereft of both parents at once, together with the usurp-

ing influence of a new baby, would be a hard pill for Junior to swallow, and Father should make every effort to give him companionship and love.

Father and the housekeeper will give Junior reassuring news about Mother's progresss—that she is happy at the hospital and will be home soon, that she asks about her little boy and will see him soon. One way for Mother and child to remain in touch is through notes carried back and forth by the father. The new baby should be mentioned occasionally. Junior might be interested to know that the baby is rather funny-looking, yet very sweet, and that his sole accomplishments are eating, sleeping, and crying.

Return of Mother and Baby

Before the baby is introduced to the first child, the latter and his Mother should have a happy reunion—just the two of them. He can cover her up when she lies down to rest a bit, and maybe put her shoes away in the closet for her. The baby can now be lovingly shown to him. Whatever his reaction, accept it as natural. Let him examine the baby for as long as he likes; since this baby belongs to him, too, he has a perfect right to touch it. If he feels a great surge of fraternal love and tries to embrace the baby, show him the spots where babies like to be kissed: top of the head, bottom of the feet. Don't force the baby on him. If he isn't particularly interested in it, who can blame him?

Be very natural when you put the baby to the breast. Whether or not Junior asks questions, tell him briefly that there is milk in the breast and that is the way babies eat. Let him get as close as he likes, so long as he doesn't interfere with the nursing. If he seems distressed by the process, it might be a good idea for the Father or the housekeeper to get him interested in something else. But he should never be barred from the room; he should be free to come and go as he likes. After the baby has finished nursing, the mother should give the older child a warm loving. He will soon accept the nursing as natural. He may express a perfectly normal desire to nurse at his mother's breast; in which case nobody should be shocked.

Mother should explain that nursing is for tiny babies only and that when he himself was a baby he got his milk in the same way. Now he is such a big boy he can drink milk from a cup.

Handling Jealousy

No matter how well the initial meeting goes off, the first youngster may show signs of being jealous of the baby after a time. But if you are prepared for this and make an effort to understand why the jealousy exists, you will be able to handle it if or when it appears.

The reason is very clear. Junior has been the only child and has had a monopoly on his parents' affections. Now he sees his father and mother infatuated with a stupid, messy baby, and it is not strange that he should feel to some degree lost and abandoned. He feels that some of the love which was his has now been transferred to the baby. He can't see that his parents love him as much as they ever did and that their love for the baby is a separate thing. As a matter of fact, you will notice that many adults who are not parents share this belief.

You will be asked many times if you don't find it difficult to pretend to love each child the same. If intelligent adults, who are impersonal about the situation in your home, can't be convinced of the truth, you can see how your older child is affected, since he is actually involved.

Therefore, it is important that you reassure him and help him to realize there is love enough for both him and the baby. Let him see your pride in him. Let him know that you enjoy talking to him and playing with him. For the first few months after the baby is born, give Junior an extra amount of time and affection.

You Needn't Feel Guilty

But certainly there should be no feeling of guilt about the second child. The love you give your youngster must be spontaneous and not appeasing. An important factor in his relationship to his brother or sister is that he must learn to accept your love for the baby. How can Junior love the baby if he never sees anyone else showing fondness for the newcomer? Your attitude should be the very natural one—that you love the baby—and you will naturally show it.

When Visitors Come

Perhaps you have handled the situation smoothly, but are worried about the effect visitors will have when they go into rhapsodies over the baby. Arrange beforehand, whenever you can, for relatives and intimate friends to bring a little token gift for the older child if they plan to bring a present for the baby. Have a supply of inexpensive toys on hand yourself, which you can dole out for the purpose if a visitor doesn't supply one. And tell everybody to please pay some attention to the older child. There may be a few undiscerning visitors who will tease Junior about his mother's having a new baby to love instead of him. Just draw Junior into your arms and say with warmth (for him) and dignity (for the offender) that Junior is your baby, too, and you will always love him with all your heart.

Suppose He Dislikes the Baby?

This may surprise you, but your problem will be simpler if Junior expressses a dislike for the baby. Instead of scolding him, be relieved that his feelings have come out into the open where you can deal with them. Explain that the baby is a part of the family, just as he is. Tell Junior that the baby will become more interesting and fun as he grows older. Right now he may not seem to have much to recommend him, but Junior was once like that and look at what a fine boy he is now.

Your first impulse when Junior tries to strike or pinch the baby will be to punish him. Instead, be understanding. Don't take it for granted that Junior was trying to hurt the baby. Show him how to pat the baby gently, praise him when he does it correctly, and hold him on your lap for a while so that he won't feel jealous and want to hurt the baby, if that was his intention.

The Less Interference the Better

Interfere as little as possible. Junior may seem to squeeze the baby too hard, but if the baby shows no discomfort, the pinch isn't really hurting. One little girl used to squeeze the baby's foot, and her mother ignored this because the baby did. After a good satisfying squeeze, the little girl would be rid of her animus and give the baby a sincerely tender and gentle hug. Every few days she would repeat the performance, each time after a longer interval, until finally she stopped altogether. At times after that, she would approach the baby with that wicked look in her eye and reach for the baby's foot. But she didn't squeeze it. She would just glare for a minute, then return to her toys.

If a child does strike or pinch so that the baby protests, give him a substitute upon which he can vent his wrath. A doll, a wooden mallet, and a block to pound are excellent. You can't have the baby hurt, of course. But giving Junior a chance to get his resentment out of his system in some harmless way, because you understand his trouble, is good emotional therapy.

Don't be sparing in praise. Go out of your way to notice and comment on Junior's desirable actions, especially any kindnesses he shows to the baby.

Caring for Two

About this time you may be wondering whether you were right, after all, in wanting your children fairly close together. With a baby and a runabout and a house to care for, it appears that someone or something is demanding your attention every second of the day. The answer, again, is planning, organization, cutting out all unnecessary motions. Otherwise you will be worn to a frazzle and nothing will be done properly.

This is a time when a good many husbands begin to feel unloved, simply because their wives are too burdened and fatigued to be interesting and attractive companions. Yet the wives need sympathy and understanding more than ever. In organizing a work schedule, take your husband into your confidence. On his next day off from work, ask him to observe you critically as you go about your tasks, and then make any suggestions he can as to ways you can cut corners. It is not only possible that he may come forth with some surprisingly good ideas, he will also see for himself what you have to contend with, and will be more understanding on days when you are exhausted. Both of you need to hang on to your sense of perspective and remember that as the children get older, the situation will get easier.

Make It Cooperative

It goes without saying that where one woman has to cope with two small children and with housekeeping, everyone should do his share. Dad can help constructively by hanging up his clothes, leaving the bathroom neat, and taking care of his belongings in the rest of the house. He can help with the children in the morning and after he gets home at night. Child rearing today is much more of a cooperative undertaking than it used to be, and if Dad investigates, he will find that many of his acquaintances are doing the same thing.

But the day-in-and-day-out care of the youngsters and the main household tasks are still the mother's job, and it is here that close study of the situation, removing points of strain wherever possible, is rewarding.

The first six weeks or so, while the new baby is finding his own rhythm and while irregularity is likely to be the rule, are bound to be busy ones. Therefore, get the house in as good shape as you can manage before the new arrival. Take a day off, if necessary, to rearrange the house so that there is a regular place for everything to go. And these places should be as convenient as possible and handy to your field of operation.

When the baby is here, and you are up and about again, you need suffer no pangs of conscience at putting the children's needs first, working in other things as you can. If you review the situation critically, you will find that about the only operations which have

to proceed on schedule are the family meals—and it won't hurt the adults to wait a while if the baby decides to eat just when you were planning to get the dinner.

Dovetailing Schedules

To follow the older child's meal and nap and bedtime routine as carefully as you can is the way to keep him happy and good-humored. Also it gives him a feeling of security in the new state of affairs. But if you have to do something for the baby at a time that conflicts, let Junior help you with it. That will make the waiting period pass more interestingly for him.

However, we believe you will find that the new baby's self-demand schedule will not interfere with the older child's as much as you might imagine. Now you understand babies. You are much better able to interpret the nature of the crying and fussing. You no longer hang anxiously over the crib to make sure the baby is breathing—you know that a normal baby can be trusted to attend to that. If Junior appears screaming, with blood running down his face, at the precise moment the baby begins to whimper, you know the baby is not going to suffer for lack of attention while you attend to Junior's wound.

You're Expert Now

Not the least of the merits of the self-demand schedule is that it gives a mother confidence to work with her baby and find out what he needs, and now you have the benefit of all that you learned from Junior. Second babies proverbially are "good" babies, swinging easily into schedules, sleeping through the night, precisely because their mothers have learned how to keep them comfortable and happy.

Since the morning, with two babies and a husband to feed, is usually one of the times of strain, make every preparation you can the night before. The table can be set, the cereal ready, dishes and utensils ready at hand.

If your husband's hours allow it, have supper as early as possible. That gives you a long evening to get the house in good condition for the morning rush.

Step Savers

When serving the family meals, filling the plates directly from the stove eliminates the washing of serving dishes. Use a large tray for carrying things to and from the table, thus saving a lot of running back and forth. Use plastic or oilcloth tablecloths or mats which can be wiped off with a damp rag, instead of a cloth which has to be washed and ironed.

At the end of a meal, but before you have your coffee, clear the table, scrape the dishes, and put them to soak in very hot suds. Then return to the table for your coffee and fifteen minutes or so of conversation with your husband. By the time you go back to

the kitchen, the dishes will be so clean from the soaking that you can remove most of them from the sink or dishpan with little scrubbing and rinse them. Let them dry in a rubber drainer—all but the silverware, which might rust—and put them away before you go to bed.

Simplicity Is the Word

Meals should be as simple as possible, composed of foods the older child can eat as well as the adults. A casserole dish, salad, fruit for dessert, and milk for the youngster are ample for a family dinner. When there are guests, provide meals that are as easy to prepare as they are delicious—roasts with baked potatoes, for instance. Use frozen and canned vegetables rather than fresh ones which you must prepare for cooking. Get everything ready that you can the day before. Don't clean the house thoroughly when you are expecting visitors. If it is picked up and dusted, it will look all right and you will be in much better spirits.

Ask the entire family to help with such things as setting the table and clearing it, picking up the living room after the guests have gone. If the guests want to take a hand, accept their help with pleasure.

The Ironing Problem

Ironing should be reduced to an irreducible minimum. The children can wear corduroy or seersucker, which requires no ironing, with polo shirts for the older child. Play clothes can be smoothed with your hands; if you hang them in the right way on the line, they may not even need this. For the time being, sheets and pillow slips can receive the same kind of treatment.

If you don't have a diaper service, and are washing diapers every evening—or morning, as you prefer—you may find it easier to wash the clothes the children have worn during the day at the same time. Thus everything is kept clean and ready for use, and you are not confronted each week with a mountainous wash. While the baby is small, there is considerable advantage in breaking big household tasks down into little ones.

Variety Helps

It is important for family morale that Mother get away from the family and her tasks now and then, if only to go to a movie while Dad baby-sits. Better yet to find a sitter you can rely upon so that Dad and Mother can go together.

And have variety in your family life. Practically no meal preparations are necessary when you have a picnic in the back yard. Dad and the older child might enjoy taking over the Saturday-night supper. Planning and ingenuity on everybody's part can turn this time of stress into one of cooperation and fun, and thereby build a happy, loving, united family.

It won't be long until the new baby is sleeping through the night and regularizing its daytime wants. These you can blend in gradually with household activities, as you did with the first youngster, and once more you can set times for tasks with a reasonable chance that you will be able to carry them out.

CHAPTER FOURTEEN

Two to three years

The second year brings a great spurt in comprehension and speech. Parents can almost see the child's understanding increase from one day to the next. It is a fascinating time. The child tries to be helpful. He will run to get his daddy's slippers at night, and empty ash trays as soon as they acquire the barest suggestion of ash. He is apt to be happy and smiling almost all day. Mother and Father congratulate themselves on having produced and trained such a wonderful child.

And then one day it happens. Mother says blithely, "Do you want to eat your lunch now?" And Junior replies just as blithely, "No." Obviously Junior didn't understand, so Mother repeats her question slowly and clearly. Junior's "no" isn't slow, but it is certainly clear. What has happened to her little boy—or girl? Did he inherit Great-uncle Albert's (on his father's side) disposition after all?

Stubborn? No, Just Normal

No, it's just that Junior has embarked upon one of those stages we mentioned in the chapter on discipline, the first of the three periods of seeming rebellion and stubbornness. The key to the situation lies in the way he made his negative response. When he said "no," he was quite happy, just as he was when he learned other new ways of behaving. And he does want his lunch. If you ignore his "no" and lead him pleasantly to the table, he is likely to climb up into his chair and eat it eagerly.

What has come over him all of a sudden? Several things. First of all, he has discovered the power of the word "no." He has seen that when other people use this magic syllable, it has a marked effect. So he tries it, too. In the exhilaration of a new accomplishment, he applies it for a while to everything that comes his way. Many observers have noted that the negative response has no relation to what a child in this phase of learning really wants. He will defend with all his might his right to say "no" and "I won't," but when grownups apparently concede this right, he will proceed quite happily to do the very thing he had refused to do.

A second element is a reaching out toward independence, another very natural manifestation whenever a youngster has mastered a number of skills and feels capable of mastering more. At two, he has conquered that long-drawn-out process of learning to walk and run. He can feed himself. He can say a number of words. He now feels competent to take into his own hands a great many services that have been performed for him by adults.

Encouraging Independence

Parents make a world of trouble for themselves when they try to suppresss these urges toward independence, on the ground that the child is not mature enough to wash himself unaided or get into his clothes by himself. They make still more trouble for themselves when they treat that "no" or "I won't" as rebellion.

Instead, let us realize that independence, and self-reliance, too, are acquired by a very long, slow process in which there is

bound to be much awkwardness in the beginning. Eventually, we certainly want a child to carry the responsibility for his own daily needs. And he feels a great sense of accomplishment in every step forward he is able to take in this respect. It gives him a sense of importance, and everyone needs to feel important.

When the urge toward independence shows itself, take this as a signal that your youngster is no longer a baby and should not be treated as one. Give him as much scope as you can to try out things for himself. If he wants to wash himself, that's wonderful. Make him feel that he has accomplished something, even though there is a ring at the neckline. Resist the temptation to continue to do everything for your youngster because it saves time. Allowing now the time it takes a small youngster to do things for himself speeds the day when he will do them efficiently and you can turn your attention to other things. But that isn't all. Allowing him to do what he can for himself is an emotional release as well. He is happy, as all of us are when we can use our powers and abilities.

There are times when adults must be firm, but this can be done in a cheerful, friendly way. When a child is given freedom of action and choice wherever possible, he actually welcomes a firm hand now and then where it is necessary for his welfare. Meanwhile, he learns from his bungling efforts even more than new skills. He learns that Dad and Mother appreciate his desire to be an upstanding individualist and that they cooperate as much as they can.

Let Him Help You

Before, after, and occasionally during this trying time, the child continues to show more and more maturity. In fact his very use

of the word "no" is an indication of his sense of being an individual capable of saying "no" as well as "yes"; in other words, making a choice. He takes a great interest in work around the house, and wants to help Mother with all her chores. Give him a child-sized broom and a little dust rag, and see how happy he is as he cleans alongside you. You can keep him from hindering you by telling him which part of the room you want him to clean.

On rainy days, after he is bored with all his toys, there is nothing so diverting as running the vacuum cleaner, shellings peas, or cleaning the bathroom floor with a scrubbing brush. If you are planning to have peas for dinner, buy a half-pound more than you usually need, to allow for the loss involved. Later, as he becomes adept at the art, he may not lose a single pea. Give him five or six pods that have already been opened and show him how to remove the peas and put them in his pan. Since the object is to amuse him, let him do anything he likes with the peas, within reason. He may spend a lot of time placing them on the table one by one, then back in the pan. When he is older he will expect the peas he has shelled to be cooked. You can usually include a handful of peas somewhere in your dinner—soups, stews, creamed dishes, salads—or cook them especially for Junior.

He may clamor to wash dishes. Roll up his sleeves, put a rubber apron on him, and show him how to wash some of your less valuable ones. Or ask him to dry some of them for you. Place a stool or chair at the sink and let him dry the pans. This is actually a help, you know. It will take him half an hour to do what you could accomplish in two minutes, but at this point the actual help rendered isn't important. It won't be long before you can trust him to wash or wipe the everyday chinaware as carefully as you do. This should all be on a voluntary basis, of course, and he should be free to quit whenever he wants. But he likes to know he is really helping.

He Can Help Daddy, Too

In the evenings and on week ends, he will be even more thrilled if he is permitted to work with his father in more manly chores. This goes for girls, too. A child can help carry out trash and do many odd jobs. In the fall, when Daddy is raking leaves, Junior will have a wonderful time loading raked-up leaves into baskets. He ought to have a small rake, too.

Often he will come up with very strange ideas and want to carry them out. The parental "no" is apt to be too automatic in these cases. Before you forbid an activity, ask yourself why. If there is no good reason why Junior shouldn't do it, let him go ahead. Also, let him take a few chances. If there is a tree with low branches in the yard and he wants to climb it, he should be free to do so. Maybe he is too little—he will find that out. Maybe he will succeed—that would be wonderful! He will come home with fewer broken bones when he is eight or nine if he is allowed to develop balance and sure-footedness from the beginning. Of course you must use judgment. If the tree is tall, you will have to put a limit on the height he should climb, and he should be shown that small branches won't hold his weight.

Dressing and Undressing

At this age he will make great strides in dressing and undressing himself. Usually the undressing comes first, and a two-year-old may undress himself repeatedly in the delight of attaining this new skill. He will also be cooperative in the dressing process, thrusting his arms into sleeves and his feet into pant legs. Presently he will want to do this "all himself," and invariably will put his arm in the wrong sleeve and both feet into one pant leg. Let him carry on alone as far as he can, but step in with a helpful word when he gets too tangled up. Trying things beyond his power is one big reason for the temper tantrums which often appear at this age. Showing him the way out of his difficulty, while giving him the idea that he is doing it himself, is a good way to avoid these.

He will try to pull on socks and should be allowed to help. You might put the sock on his foot, his part of the job being to pull it up. He can slip his foot into his shoe while you hold back the tongue.

Buttons and laces will be beyond his powers for some time, but you can illustrate the process by which the button is put through the hole, and encourage his efforts to master it. When he reaches the stage of being able to get into his clothes unaided, he will put some on backward or wrong side out. If he is just going to play around the house, let these mistakes go unless they hamper his movements. Be all encouragement for any successes achieved. Later, when there is no danger of his refusing to try any more, you can tactfully help him put on his clothes in the way they are intended to be worn.

Temper Tantrums Have a Meaning

It is during this age, when youngsters are trying to master a number of new, difficult skills and also to achieve a certain level of independence, that we used to expect temper tantrums to occur. Parents were counseled not to be alarmed when their preschooler exploded into violent wrath, threw himself on the floor, and kicked and screamed. It was regarded as a normal phase, and one that would pass provided the youngster was not allowed to gain his end by such a socially undesirable way of acting.

With greater study of children, temper tantrums are now viewed in a somewhat different light. Quite often they happen when a little fellow has tackled something that is too much for his powers. They happen when parents tell him what to do all the time and fail to realize that the youngster should have more freedom of choice. They happen when parents use force instead of tact to get obedience. They happen when children are overexcited or tired. The nervous system of the small child is not yet very stable. When he is frustrated or upset, he is likely to react in a way that will make everybody sit up and take notice.

If your child begins having temper tantrums, try to find out what causes them. If he has been overwhelmed by the perversity of an inanimate object, quietly show him the way to deal with the balky plaything or material. If the tantrums are his answer to your commands, try issuing fewer commands. Instead, engage his interest in whatever it is you want him to do, offering it as an attractive opportunity rather than a boring duty. If you must interrupt his play, make it seem that you are doing him a favor. "Darling, come see the surprise I have for you at the table," is likely to make him come running, where a brusque "Stop what you are doing, it's lunchtime," may infuriate him. And it's elementary that a quiet, stable routine, providing meals and rest at wisely spaced intervals, is a help in keeping a youngster happy and good-natured.

You should certainly take the tantrum itself in calm fashion; there is no harm in being friendly about it. The emotionally overwrought youngster may respond to the comfort of his mother's lap. But if he kicks at you and pushes you away, best leave him alone until the fireworks begin to subside. Then you can receive him into your society again in a cheerful, accepting manner. But do try to see if you can't remove the causes for most of his temper tantrums.

Interest In Toilet Training

At some point during this year, and in some cases even a little earlier, he will decide of his own accord to begin to use the toilet. You should have a toilet seat ready—either the kind that fits on the regular toilet or a little chair with a potty underneath. His readiness to use the toilet is apt to come very suddenly. He will tell you in words or signs that he wants to use the toilet, or he may simply climb on when you are nowhere around. Of course, you will express your pleasure over this accomplishment, and you will continue your praise —though not to an excessive degree—until self-toileting has become an old story. He will have accidents now and then, but that's only to be

expected. Ignore the lapses and praise him when he remembers. Even though you show no signs of displeasure, he may feel guilty when he urinates on the floor and will want to make amends by cleaning up. Show him a place where he can always find a rag for such use.

Bed-wetting

Your child may have toilet-trained himself completely for the daytime hours, but will still wet at night. You can try waking him and carrying him into the bathroom just before you go to bed. If he is too sleepy to perform, or is antagonistic, put him back to bed. Try again a few nights later. This seems to work better when the child is not exposed to a bright light on his nocturnal jaunt. You will need some sort of illumination so that you can see what you are doing; perhaps a light in an adjacent room will be sufficient.

If he falls asleep while he is on the toilet or refuses to urinate, hold him on your lap for a minute and let him feel your affection. Then return him to the toilet and gently tell him what he is supposed to do. If he does, praise him. If he doesn't, forget about it. Leave him on the toilet just for a minute or two, unless he is eliminating, in which case, he may need more time. Put diapers on him at night until he has definitely established the habit of remaining dry. Even after this has been attained, don't be shocked if he wets his bed once in a while for a few years, especially when he has a cold or is upset about something.

You will save him possible humiliation if you teach him a word that everyone will recognize for his toilet needs. "Urinate" is both simple and understandable. A private family word is natural enough, but occasionally Junior will be with other people who won't

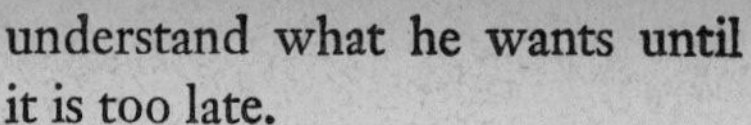

understand what he wants until it is too late.

Companionship with Dad

As the child leaves babyhood behind him, he will be increasingly aware of other people. At first it is his mother to whom he gives all his love, since it is usually upon her that he must depend for his needs, his daily comfort, and fun. But at about the age of two, a little girl begins to turn to her father for companionship while a boy is still closer to his mother. This is a healthy sign. A girl learns from her father, as well as from her mother, what it means to be a woman, and a boy learns to understand the role of a man in family life. Later, the boy will turn to his father and the girl to her mother as the person he or she wants to be like when he grows up. A parent who understands this pattern of emotional growth will not feel hurt if his two- or three-year-old seems less affectionate than before, but will maintain a close relationship to the child during this time when the child may center his attention on the other parent. For children do need the affection and support of both parents.

Week-end Excursions

Since Father is away from home so much of the time, one of the best ways for him to give his children the companionship they need from him is to plan excursions on week ends. These should be special times for him to share with his boy or girl without Mother. The outings should be planned around the child's age, interests, and stamina. A three-year-old would find no pleasure in a ball game, of course; neither should he be expected to enjoy an extended trip to the zoo, much as he loves animals. When you do take him to the zoo, make allowances for time spent in transportation, and plan to take in only two or three exhibits. If he is perfectly happy just watching the monkeys, try limiting the sight-seeing to that the first time. Or if you take him to an amusement park, he may want to spend all his time riding in the little train or on the merry-go-round.

A city child will love to go to a farm on the outskirts of town to see the farm animals. Just being with Daddy will make the child happy. Show him that you like to be with him. Even a walk together, with the child chattering about anything and everything, should be very satisfying to you both.

When Daddy and child return home, Junior will probably want to tell Mother all about the jaunt. She should listen with interest, but she shouldn't ask too many questions if the information isn't forthcoming. Let the jaunt be Daddy's and Junior's, or Daddy's and Betty's, as the case may be.

Playing with Other Children

When your child reaches the age of two, it is fine if several mothers can arrange to take turns being in charge at playtime. Mothers in many communities throughout the country have organized cooperative play groups, patterning them on well-established and well-run nursery schools. If you are interested in organizing a nursery-school group, write to your local Health and Welfare Department or State Department of Education for information. (Also see the bibliography on page 235 for a list of books on nursery schools.) Such a group gives each mother a wonderful chance to have a quiet morning or afternoon. (Have you forgotten such a thing exists?)

The supervision involved, when your turn comes around, should be kept to a minimum. Your function is to see that the children don't wander off and that they don't get into any serious difficulty. There should be enough toys to go around; perhaps each child can bring one with him. They should even be allowed in most cases to fight things out for themselves. You should keep a watchful eye on them, but not interfere unless there is really danger of harm being done.

Rather than having them running in and out of the house all the time, make a rule that on nice days they stay outdoors and on rainy days they stay in a designated part of the house. You can qualify this, if you like, by allotting each child, one at a time, one trip into the kitchen for a drink of water or short conversation, and, of course, a trip to the toilet when necessary. You'll probably want to give them milk or juice and crackers halfway through the morning, and we suggest that all liquid be given in paper or plastic cups.

When There Are Only Two

At this age, play is more likely to be by twos than as a group. There are fewer complications when your child is playing with one youngster, but even so there may be days when they don't get along at all and there is constant bickering and crying. On such occasions, separate them. One can remain outside while the other plays in the house. Tell them that is the way it is going to be until they can play together happily. You will find that the most violent quarrel will be forgotten quickly, and the two will greet each other with cries of joy when the ban is lifted, which may be anywhere from three minutes to ten minutes, though it can be longer if the children are happy to play separately.

Nursery School

Nursery schools provide fine opportunities for children to learn to play well together. The teachers in good nursery schools understand and love children and know how to handle them. There are play facilities at nursery school that few parents can provide, and the children are encouraged to develop their abilities and talents, to grow in independence, and to get along with others. The start they get here in social behavior paves the way for good adjustment in kindergarten and first grade.

The child's introduction to nursery school should be managed carefully. He may be ready for it at three or a little before, or he may not be ready for another six months or more. The only way to tell is by watching his reactions carefully. He may be the outgoing type who will march up to the door, wave good-by to Mamma—and that's that. But many children are more timid, and will be too frightened to enter into the school activities unless Mother is somewhere about. So go with the child and be prepared to stay for a few days until he begins to adapt himself to the change. Then when you leave, don't sneak away. He may be playing happily, but when he notices your absence he may be upset and frightened. Tell him casually that you are leaving but will come back for him later, then go quickly. Sometimes a mother has to spend several days at nursery school with the child before he is weaned of his need for her.

Habit Exchange

The nursery-school teacher may warn you in advance that your youngster will pick up bad habits from the other children, and she is right. Your consolation is that your child will also learn desirable things from his companions. Your child, for instance, who is your pride and joy because he speaks so plainly, may come home from nursery school with an unintelligible lisp. For the most part, ignore such things. They will soon pass. Remind yourself of all the benefits nursery school is giving him.

It is far more important that he is learning to adjust to other children, learning to express himself in stories, music, and play, accepting wholesome routines under the stimulus of the group, and having the best time a small child can have.

If He's Overstimulated

Even the child who loves the school and who fits in well may put you through a very bad first week because he is overstimulated. Don't withdraw him from school because of this. So long as he is happy there, he will soon adjust. If the condition persists after the first week, perhaps the entire school program is too much for him. Limit his stay accordingly. If two hours a day seem about right, then bring him home when the two hours are up. As he grows older, the time spent at school can be lengthened.

Body Curiosity

When a child examines his body or those of other children, he is satisfying a natural curiosity. The genital area is interesting to him because that is where he eliminates, and it is situated in a difficult place to examine. If any of his playmates are of the opposite sex, he will be interested in their genital differences and will wonder about them. Explain to your little girl that boys and men have a penis, whereas women and girls do not; otherwise, she may feel there is something the matter with her. Little girls should understand that there is nothing wrong with their not having a penis. Matter-of-fact explanations of these matters when they first come up may save a child worry and self-torture.

During the process of learning about his body, a child is very apt to handle his genitals. To him, this is in the same category as playing with his toes and feet, which for a time are fascinating objects. After a while you will notice that he stops putting his big toe in his mouth and goes on to other diversions. In the same way he

will exhaust his curiosity about his genitals unless his explorations are sharply frustrated. If he is scolded or punished, he will not understand why, will be hurt, and will be apt to cling to this type of play.

When you see your small child handling himself, try not to pay too much attention. Either ignore his action entirely or quietly start him in some kind of play. Don't scold, don't give him the idea there is anything wrong or bad about this part of the body.

It May Be Anxiety

The case is somewhat different when a youngster of two or three is handling himself at every opportunity, but shaming and punishment are still the worst possible ways to treat the situation. Most children who masturbate excessively are reacting to strain or insecurity. Maybe there is tension in the household, which they are helpless to do anything about. Often the child who masturbates excessively is afraid to tackle the world outside himself, because he has met with too much rebuff and failure. Consult your doctor or a child-guidance specialist to learn wise ways to deal with the situation. In any event, try to encourage your child in wider interests and activities, in a loving, kindly way. Every youngster needs plenty of enjoyable things to do; he needs above all to feel happy and secure and well loved.

Where There's No Place to Play

When we have talked about play, we have taken it for granted that there is a portion of the yard that can be fenced in (this should be done for children under three) and at least a corner of a room that can be made an indoor play space. Every child is entitled to such an arrangement. But we realize that today many parents cannot provide such play space.

Perhaps you live in an apartment, maybe in a single room. There is no yard, no roof that can be used as a safe play place. Your problem is a child always underfoot. This becomes nerve-racking for the most devoted mother, and children are likely to get whiny and demanding. In addition to the problem of a bored child pulling at your skirts and wishing to be amused, you may also feel that you are failing to do a good job of child rearing.

A Joint Effort

If there are other mothers with the same problem in your vicinity, why not get together? We have mentioned the possibility of a group of mothers sharing the care of children on alternate mornings. In this case, the mother in charge might take a group to a park, playground, or play street, or supervise their play on a sidewalk if nothing better offers. Many mothers have solved difficult situations by cooperative effort. It's worth trying!

If this is not possible, we suggest that you draw on your ingenuity, organizing power, and good humor. We have mentioned before that small children like to be allowed to participate in whatever the adults are doing. To give children a share in adult activities takes time and patience in the early stages, but it is richly rewarding.

Using Your Ingenuity

You can't play with your child all day, and even if you could, constant amusement of this kind would not be good for him. It is much better for him to learn, in a happy way, that there are certain tasks about the house which must be performed before

Mother can play. If Mother gives him a part in these tasks, he will feel a sense of importance and at the same time be happily occupied.

When breakfast is over, and Mother prepares a dessert or casserole dish for supper, Junior can operate an egg beater or hand Mother the pans she needs. He can even stand on a chair at the sink to wash dishes, or help her with cleaning jobs. Setting the table is a task with which children of this age can help.

He can also wield a long-handled duster; or, perched on a stool at the sink or lavatory, he can wash clothes—a pair of socks or an undershirt, for example. Given a damp cloth, he can wipe his own finger marks off the woodwork. He can also empty ash trays and wastebaskets.

The tasks assigned him should be ones he wants to do, and when he becomes bored with working, he should be free to wander off to his own toys and amuse himself with them. But when he shows a desire to help again, the wise mother will provide him with tasks.

Time Out Together

The child whose mother must work all morning is entitled to some free time with her in the afternoon, and her work schedule should be arranged with this in mind. Whenever weather permits, this free time should be spent in the open air. You can go to the park, or saunter to the grocery store for your marketing, or call on friends who have small children, or just sit on the porch while Junior runs and plays under your watchful eye.

When the weather is bad, give him plenty of attention in the afternap hours. Since fresh air will do wonders for you both, put on wraps and open the windows for a while. This is a good time to do exercises together. The rest of the time be prepared to be an appreciative audience, even though you do not enter into all his games. When Dad comes home, he may want a fifteen-minute rest and then be ready to take over, for by this time any mother will need a vacation from her offspring. While Dad supervises the bath and story time, Mother can be preparing supper.

Introducing the three-year-old

Three is a delightful age. A child has greater self-control, is friendly and cooperative, and is learning to manage social relationships. Let's follow him through a typical day.

Frequently whines and fusses upon awakening. May drowse off after getting mother's help in toileting.

Cheers up when fully awake. Likes to frisk around parents' room and get dressed with them.

Can put on pants, socks, shoes, sweater. Able to undress easily, undo buttons—but can't button them.

Appetite usually good for breakfast. Feeds himself skillfully—not much parental help is needed.

Will cooperate in clearing the table, tidying his own room—if asked.

Sometimes creates imaginary playmates, pets, or pretends that he is an animal.

Alternates between pestering brothers and sisters and getting along with them.

Learning to ride tricycle. Likes to go marketing with mother.

Requests favorite foods (such as fruit, meat, milk) when meal is being prepared.

Gaining good control of elimination. Frequently has bowel movement after lunch.

Willing to rest at naptime but frequently does not go to sleep.

Beginning to be able to play with other children, as well as beside them, Has definite choice in friends.

Needs guidance when play gets quarrelsome. Aggressiveness now expressed in words as well as actions.

Notices sex differences and sometimes worries about them. Questions should be answered simply.

May handle genitals. Can be quite matter-of-factly distracted from sex play.

Enjoys painting, crayoning, modeling with clay. Results seldom resemble what he calls them.

Welcomes playtime with his father. Likes riddles and enjoys guessing games.

Likes to have familiar stories read without change. Enjoys explaining pictures.

Listens to adults. Wants to please and enjoys praise. Likes to master new words.

Affectionate toward parents. Mother is generally the favorite.

Likes to help prepare his bath, wash himself. Gets out unwillingly.

May try to be the center of attention if eating with family. Eats well by himself.

Outcropping fears: of the dark, dogs, other animals, fire engines. Needs reassurance.

When he knows parents are going out may say good-by cheerfully. Or may protest until older.

Plays in bed for half-hour or so. Usually goes to sleep without too many demands.

Begins to talk about his dreams and may occasionally be wakened in fright by nightmare.

Frequently gets up during night. May get out of bed and wander oround the house.

May want to get in bed with mother. But can usually be diverted if parent stays with him a while.

CHAPTER FIFTEEN

Age three to five

At three, the child continues to make great progress in adding new words to his vocabulary, and now begins to work on his grammar. If you have ever struggled with the complicated tenses of a foreign language, you will be awed by the ease with which your youngster will pick up the past, present, future, and even subjunctive of English, which to him is just as foreign as French or Spanish is to you. And now that he has more or less mastered his language problem, he begins to talk all the time. You used to greet with joy every word that emerged from his baby lips; now there are times when you wonder if he will ever *stop* talking.

He asks question after question, and repeats the same ones time and time again. You may feel as if you are being cross-examined by a shrewd attorney who is trying to trap you into making contradictory statements. The child's technique seems to be, first, a rapid-fire string of innocent questions which invariably require an affirmative answer. Then when you are numb and automatically say "yes" without thinking, he asks a question to which your answer would not be "yes." This furnishes good mental exercise for parents.

Whenever the child is really asking for information, he should be answered carefully and truthfully. But when he begins to ask questions without listening to or caring about the answers, help him find something to do.

Make-believe

What is true and what is make-believe is not entirely clear to the child of three to five. The world is a strange and wonderful place to him and anything might happen. When he announces that a hungry tiger is in the bathroom, don't punish him for telling untruths. Simply enter into the fun and hand Junior an imaginary steak to take to the tiger.

The time will probably come when your child will declare he has done something he hasn't. Perhaps you tell him that when he has picked up a few toys he can have a cookie, and after a few minutes he comes into your room and tells you his toys are in order. But when you step into his room you find the toys still underfoot. Instead of scolding him, you should point out that he just pretended to pick up his toys, so now you will give him a "pretend" cookie. That will show him the difference between real and make-believe better than a million words.

Tall Tales

Perhaps your child will tell you fabulous tales of his adventures and expect you to listen and contribute appropriate exclamations. If you get the impression that he is beginning to believe in these imaginary escapades, you may point out that although he hasn't really done these things, he tells wonderful stories and you like to listen to them. You might also transform the actual day's happenings into story form to help him draw the distinction.

Some children even go so far as to have imaginary playmates. These playmates are most important to them. Mother may have to set an extra place at the table. Father may be told tearfully that he is sitting on the imaginary child. The companionship of other youngsters will usually help the child to outgrow his need for nonexistent playmates. Sometimes a pet will furnish the interest and companionship the child requires.

Meeting Destructiveness

The child of this age can also be destructive at times. He removes strips of perfectly good wallpaper. He smears ink over the desk. He hacks away with scissors at his hair and other convenient objects. He smears the sofa with cold cream. He takes your food chopper apart and buries the pieces in different parts of the garden, then forgets where they are. Any bright, active child in this period of eager exploration is almost sure to upset adult concerns in some way because he lacks experience and judgment. The best thing to do is to substitute permissible play and exploration for that which is destructive. When he wants to play with water, give it to him in a big pan in the backyard, or let him wash some tins in the sink. Tack a large piece of cardboard or construction paper on his playroom wall and explain that this is his special place for exercising his artistic talents. Find time toward the end of the morning to build a house in the sand pile or to roll a ball. Or take him for a ride around the block in his gocart.

Eating

A decline in appetite is normal around three to four. There are two reasons for this. The child isn't growing nearly as rapidly, and his interest is attracted by many things, so that he is unable to concentrate on such prosaic business as putting food into his mouth. His mind is moving in leaps and bounds, and he is full of questions even during mealtime. Give him small helpings of food, arranged attractively on his plate, and let him decide how much he wants to eat. If he eats that and wants more, give it to him, but don't try to force him to finish even the first plateful, no matter how small an amount of food is there. The three-year-old often requires less than half the food his baby brother or sister eats per day.

It is normal for appetite to operate by fits and spurts at this age, and is nothing to be troubled about. Junior may pick at his food for a day or two, and then gobble it down and call for more for another day or two. So long as he is happy and healthy and full of bounce, he can be counted upon to eat as much as he needs.

But a child under emotional tension, or upset from some physical cause, occasionally will not eat enough. If a child refuses three meals in a row, or over a period of days takes in only a few mouthfuls, it is well to consult your doctor. The proper amount of food is important from the standpoint of both health and disposition.

The Vegetable Problem

Some children of this age refuse to eat vegetables, and mothers may find it hard to maintain a balanced diet. The answer is to use your ingenuity to slip a variety of vegetables into the diet in ways the youngster will accept. Many children will eat carrots and the like in a flavorful stew or soup or meat loaf, while rejecting them in identifiable form. At this age, too, they are likely to eat vegetables raw and refuse them when cooked. You can tempt Junior with flowerlets of cauliflower, wedges of raw tomato, crisp carrot and celery sticks. It is also a good idea to offer him several vegetables, both raw and cooked, and let him make his own choice among them.

Thinly sliced raw vegetables can be inserted in sandwiches. Most preschoolers love fruit, so if vegetable consumption drops temporarily, vitamins can be supplied by letting the youngster fill up on fruit cocktail and fruit salads, and letting him munch apples or other fruits between meals.

Play and Responsibility

The youngster's play interests widen, necessitating a larger range of play materials. Indoors, he will want to create, and he should be given coloring devices, paper, blunt-tipped scissors. He will love small, colored blocks of assorted shapes and sizes, as well as large building blocks. Little boys and girls both will enjoy very simple dollhouses and construction toys (which should be sturdy ones).

The three-year-old, with his vivid imagination, enjoys toys that lend themselves to imaginative play, such as a miniature doctor's or nurse's kit, automobiles, trains, airplanes. Little boys like to make-believe that they are policemen or cowboys or soldiers and enjoy small holster sets. Little girls will play by the hour that they are mothers or nurses, dressing and undressing their dolls, feeding them, putting them to bed. (Many little boys like dolls, too, and that is all right and perfectly natural.) Replicas of household machinery, such as stoves and vacuum cleaners, pans, dishes, garden tools, also provide many happy hours.

Outdoor Toys

Out of doors, the youngster will enjoy simple wheel toys, a tricycle, a teeter-totter, a sandbox, a wading pool, and a climbing device of some kind. Several families might cooperate to build or buy climbing apparatus, which youngsters adore, and upon which they will learn to perform surprising feats of agility. Slides are very popular with children of this age. Around three and a half, any form of outdoor gymnastic equipment that the child can enjoy may be installed.

Both the outdoor and indoor play spaces should be places where the youngster can play safely, untrammeled by "don't's." Fishponds and any other holes, no matter how shallow, should be drained and covered. The yard should be regularly scoured for broken glass and other dangerous things. All boards must be examined for protruding nails.

Since children of three or more grow proficient at opening doors and gates, you will have to teach your youngster to stay within certain boundaries as soon as he is able to go in and out of the house at will. This is especially important for families who live directly on the street or with no enclosed yards. To satisfy wanderlust, accompany the child on exploratory walks around the neighborhood, and impress upon him that he is not to cross a street unless an adult is with him.

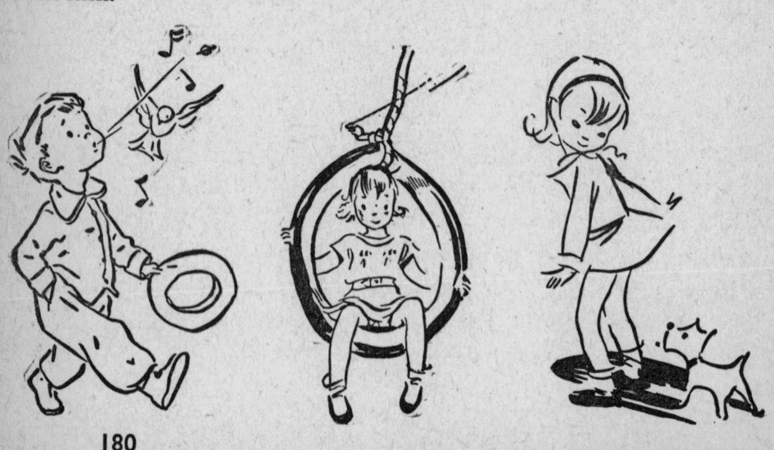

A pet will often serve to keep a child contented in his own yard. You can teach Junior how to be gentle with animals and how to care for them. He is too young to accept much responsibility in the care of his pet, but you should foster the beginnings of such responsibility. The child should know that animals must be fed regularly, housebroken, and given love and attention. Encourage Junior to help you care for the pet.

Pleasure Chores

Special chores, well within the limits of a child's ability, are actually enjoyed. When one chore begins to pall and seems like drudgery, give him something else to do. Your youngster can be in charge of emptying ash trays and placing them at strategic points around the house; he can help set the table for dinner; he can bring in the morning paper or the mail. You will be able to think of many similar tasks for him. All of them should be broached in a matter-of-fact way, with expressions of gratitude at their completion.

He can even help a little with a younger baby, but of course the responsibility is yours. You should not ask too much, and you should be very grateful when the older child does help. Avoid making a younger brother or sister a burden and you will be surprised to find how well the older child can amuse the baby at times.

Suggested Schedule

After breakfast, the youngster of three or more can wipe up any food he spilled on table or floor, and then brush his teeth. It is now believed that the best time for teeth cleaning is directly after meals. The earlier this habit is established, the better. The child will dress himself, with just a little help from you. Then out of doors for play, until he is tired. He may need a quiet period before lunch, during which he sits or lies down with a picture book or doll. Lunch can be quite simple, but must be nourishing: soup, sandwich, salad, fruit, leftovers, milk—any combination of these that helps furnish his daily requirements.

His nap should be taken in a quiet room. He will probably stop sleeping soon, but he will still need a rest. A soft toy or a picture book will help him to be quiet for half or three-quarters of an hour.

When naptime is over, he can walk, play, or go visiting with his mother. Usually you should plan to be free to be with him, and the type of amusement should be of his choosing.

Zero Hour

He may be slightly fussy (or even very fussy) during the half hour or so preceding dinner, just when you are busiest. You might try having him sit in the kitchen where he can watch you while you tell him a story. If you are the type of woman who can't keep her mind on the three bears and at the same time remember how many measures of coffee you put in the coffee pot, this solution obviously won't work for you. If he insists on being near you, however, you can attempt a running commentary on your activities of the moment, being as dramatic as you like. Or give the child crayons and paper or other materials for quiet play.

If your husband walks in on you as you are becoming dramatic on How to Cook a Pork Chop, he may consider you slightly mad, but this risk is worth while if it keeps Junior amused and happy during dinner preparations. Father's arrival frees the mother for a while. You may have to do a bit of juggling with bath and supper, and this is where Father can help tremendously by giving the youngster his bath. Often, the bath soothes and rests the child so that he eats his dinner happily.

You will find yourself adjusting the child's entire routine to meet changes in his development and the effects of outside influence.

Perl

If the child suddenly becomes uncooperative, it may help to change his schedule a bit. Sometimes children need more rest for a while, or perhaps a change in the time for naps. Be on the lookout for points of strain and tension, analyze them, and one by one eliminate possible causes. By now you should automatically be able to reel off the daily necessities for every child: adequate rest, well-balanced meals, regular routine, happy home atmosphere, wholesome social relationships outside the home, parental interest in the child's activities, understanding of his capabilities. The last—understanding of his capabilities—may be hardest for parents. Junior is so bright about so many things, we tend to expect too much wisdom from him in matters he has not yet had the opportunity or experience to be wise about.

Questions on Reproduction

We dealt with this in Chapter Thirteen, "A New Baby in the Family"—but suppose your Junior is an only child or was too young to understand when the little brother or sister arrived.

When a mother is pregnant, both she and her husband expect the older child to ask a few questions and are more or less prepared with the answers. But when the first question appears, parents sometimes make a bid for time by saying that they will answer "later." The child senses the tension and may not ask the question again. If neither parent feels he can bring up the matter in a natural way, we advise you to buy one of the books written for little children that tell the story of birth, and read it to your youngster. The book you choose should be geared to the age of your child. For the three-to-five-year group, the most elementary book is all that is necessary, but be sure it gives the facts in a clear, simple way. The very young child just needs to be told that babies grow inside their mothers, that they start as tiny eggs, and that fathers furnish seeds to make the eggs grow.

Pets will help teach children about birth. If your cat or a neighbor's is expecting kittens, explain to the child that the animal is carrying her babies inside her and let the child feel them gently through the furry wall. If it is the animal's first litter, do not plan to have your child watch the birth process. But an animal who has had a good many litters produces babies easily, and the child will be fascinated as he watches the young emerge and be cleaned up by their mother.

Nervous Habits

It is not uncommon, between the ages of three and four, for a variety of nervous habits to show up. These include such things as face twitching (tic), nail biting, sometimes stammering. Most children who have been thumb suckers previously drop the practice around this age, but some who have not sucked their thumbs before begin to do so now.

These are usually signs of nervous tension, outcome of the fact that three-to-four-year-olds are geared to such a high pitch of mental and physical activity. If your child begins to stutter now, after having talked normally up to this time, it is probably for this reason.

The nervous habit in itself can be ignored, but it is well to see if you can calm the youngster down a bit by interspersing periods of rest and quiet play among his more strenuous activities. He needs twelve hours in bed each night at this age, and an afternoon rest or

nap period. If he is getting this and still shows signs of tension, break the morning and afternoon outdoor play by short sessions indoors with books or dolls or art materials. And be careful not to exert too much pressure of any kind.

If he stutters, do not correct him; just speak slowly yourself —and don't talk too much. Stammering that is a nervous habit usually disappears somewhere between four and five, if not before. If it continues, a speech expert should be consulted.

Dawdling

One of the most annoying features of this otherwise fascinating age period is the dawdling over necessary operations. About the time Junior has become really proficient in dressing, undressing, and feeding himself, he may begin drawing out these processes to fantastic lengths. There are two reasons for this. First, he is inclined to lose interest in any technique he has mastered. Second, his mind is too full of many other things to concentrate on the job in hand.

Even though you allow a youngster in the dawdling period all the time you can, there are occasions when you must speed him up. You might do this by standing by and handing him the next garment he is to put on. A child who has a strong desire to do things for himself may be spurred by the suggestion that you will have to dress him if he doesn't step on it. You must be careful, however, not to make him dependent upon you for these routines.

Mealtime can be patience-trying indeed at this stage of development. Junior may proclaim his hunger loudly, then not touch a bit of food when you put his meal before him. He plays with objects on the table and carries on an enthralling conversation, while the food you have prepared so carefully grows cold and unappetizing. This is quite a different situation from the one where a youngster does not want his food. Now he wants the food—but it takes him forever to get around to eating it.

With my children, I found it desirable to remove from the table anything that might engage attention, and to discourage conversation. In addition, we fell back on a time-honored trick of showing our little dawdler the hands on a clock, and allowing one half-hour for the meal. Our three-and-a-half-year-old learned that when the minute hand reached a certain place, the plate would be whisked away. If she was hungry, the food would vanish in about the last five minutes of this period. If she was not hungry, she had the privilege of passing up the meal.

Let Him Take the Consequences

Children learn after a while that they cheat themselves of play and other fun by lingering so long over things like meals and dressing. So far as possible, the dawdling child should take the consequences of his slowness. If it's an expedition planned for the youngster's enjoyment, Mother can point out sadly that Junior just didn't get ready in time. When the children outside call for him to come out and play, it is Junior's loss if he fools the morning away getting into his clothes. Some children have to accept the penalty for being late to school several times before they realize that it is up to them to hurry into their clothes. Do not nag the dawdling child. Quietly letting him take the penalties of dawdling will cure him of it in time.

A pictorial guide

to the four-year-old

Every four-year-old is different; yet studies of thousands of children of this age show that they have certain abilities, interests, and characteristics in common. It is a help to parents to know what in general to expect.

Generally wakes in morning in cheerful humor. Takes care of own immediate needs.

Can almost completely dress himself if clothes are ready at hand.

Very energetic. Adept on tricycle and climbing apparatus. Can handle some simple tools.

Enjoys nursery school or a play group, since he usually prefers play with others to solitary play.

Growing verbal ability. Sometimes expressed in such ways as quarreling, tattling.

Play still needs some supervision. Quarrels may lead to too much hitting, kicking, throwing.

Verbally—and sometimes physically—child dissents from his mother's authority.

He is beginning to understand rules and restrictions, such as balls for throwing—not blocks.

Frequently annoys older brothers and sisters, bullies younger ones.

Appetite is fair but improving. Has definite likes and dislikes. Eats skillfully.

Frequently wants toilet privacy but asks for help with wiping. Controls urination.

Will rest after lunch, but seldom naps. Plays quietly with books, toys.

Vivid imagination is frequently expressed in dramatic play, imitation of adults.

Boys may play with dolls, girls with boyish toys. All right if each enjoys his own toys, too.

Works hard at drawing—though he may change theme in middle. Details are crude.

Likes to try musical instruments, play phonograph. Takes part in singing games.

Makes intricate buildings with blocks. Admires his own work. Likes to have father help.

A peak age for crying and whining if bored or hurt. Needs comforting, then distraction.

Listens with interest to verse and action stories—especially those explaining how things work.

Child is continually asking questions—both to get information and to make conversation.

Child frequently clings affectionately to parents. Likes to be cuddled. Enjoys tumbling.

May confuse parents' answers about how babies are born with stories picked up elsewhere.

Bathing, toileting of both sexes together offer healthy ways to teach sex differences.

Can bathe himself if mother supervises. Can also partially dry himself.

Enjoys eating with family. But interrupts progress of meal by talking, leaving table.

Shows fear of dark, animals, fire engines, old people. May resent mother's going out.

Goes to bed without serious objections—especially if he can recognize bedtime on clock.

Less awakening because of nightmares now. May wake to go to toilet, needs help getting back.

CHAPTER SIXTEEN

Five to six

It may not happen on your child's fifth birthday, but very soon now you are going to receive your reward for the patience, understanding, and forbearance you have been called upon to exercise so many times in the preceding years. For it is somewhere around the age of five that most children complete the long, toilsome process of getting their bodies under control and of adjusting to the world immediately around them.

Five is a definite division point between babyhood and childhood. Up until then, the average child is a mixture of both. He will display babyish traits at times, even while he is reaching forward to a new stage of maturity. When he becomes absorbed in learning to dress himself, he may regress in toilet training or in some other phase that formerly held his interest. He may revert to thumb sucking when he is tired or when things become too much for him.

But around five years of age, the whole process of growing into childhood seems to crystallize and, as a general rule, baby ways are left behind. The five-year-old is surer of himself, and no longer needs to make the strong bid for independence that we noted in the year between two and three. If pressed too far, he may rebel and say "I won't," but the rebellion is of short duration. He is anxious to please, to conform to adult requirements.

Knows What Is Real

The imaginative flights of three to four have now served their purpose. He is able to distinguish between what is real and what is make-believe, and his present interest is learning about the real world. His questions reveal a true thirst for knowledge. In fact, stories that soar too far beyond the believable are likely to offend him. He loves to hear about real-life people and real activities like farming, steam engines, airplanes.

Quick Dresser Now

His body has become an efficient little machine. He can run and play without continually falling down and bruising himself. His fingers are skillful enough to handle small tasks, such as lacing a shoe or buttoning a button. Dressing is no longer a major operation, full of obstacles and frustrations, but something to be accomplished easily and quickly. The five-year-old can take care of nearly all his personal needs, especially if clothes are laid out so that he can distinguish front from back, and shoes are marked so that he can distinguish right from left.

He can put his clothes and toys away in orderly fashion, and enjoys doing it if places have been provided and it has been made a natural part of the day's routine. He loves to help with household tasks and to make himself useful in any way he can.

He has a working vocabulary that is equal to any ordinary situation—two thousand words is the average at this age—and can hold his own in a conversation. He may want to monopolize it, in fact, but that is only because he has a good command of language and many ideas that he wants to express.

Becomes Robust

He takes on a new robustness physically, as well. Around four and a half, you may have noticed an increase in appetite and interest in food. Around five, this becomes stabilized, and the finicky appetite that often characterizes children of three and four is apt to turn into zest for at least two meals every day. (Around six, we might add, he is likely to become a notable trencherman, for another growth spurt begins then.) Except for bouts with children's diseases such as measles, mumps, whooping cough, chicken pox—which he is likely to go through as his circle of playmates enlarges—he is seldom sick.

The five-year-old is no longer as bent on exploration and adventuring as he was at four. He is interested in his home and in developing activities that center there. Usually there is a particularly strong bond with the mother at this time. He likes to be with her, to share what she is doing. Quite often he announces that he is going to marry her when he grows up. Father may be a bit left out while this is going on, though Junior respects and admires his paternal parent as much as ever and boasts to companions of his prowess. Out of his very love and preoccupation with Mother, Junior may be critical of her at times, for he is extremely sensitive to her approval or disapproval. But no mother should be disconcerted by being told she is

"mean." Junior doesn't really believe that. Nor need she be afraid that he is turning into a "Mamma's boy." This is a phase of normal development, and mothers are entitled to enjoy it to the full.

Naturally Nice

Parents are inclined to plume themselves upon the success of whatever child-rearing methods they used, when the happy state of fiveness is reached. And we would not deprive you of that pleasure. But the truth is that unless a child has been grossly mishandled, neglected, or abused, he will naturally become amenable and easy to live with around the age of five. This is one of the stages in his development when his whole being is more or less in balance, a kind of plateau in the growth process. Soon, other vigorous thrusts forward will appear, with their characteristic behavior patterns—the smarty stage, the roughneck stage, for instance, all playing their part in development as have the stages that went before. In fact, a change toward more assertiveness begins to show itself around five and a half. And that will not mean that you have failed, or that yours is going to be a problem youngster. It will just mean that your youngster is growing in the way that children do.

There may be a few things now that will trouble you. The mysterious fears that so often bedevil younger children—the possible product, as we mentioned earlier, of the vastness of the adjustments they are required to make—will probably have vanished. But the five-year-old may become afraid of something real and visible, such a thunder or lightning. This is part of an adjustment to an outside world of which he is more aware. The five-year-old may also have nightmares in which he dreams

that a bear or wolf is after him, and waken screaming. The parents should be comforting, of course. They should also try to eliminate anything that is causing fear and anxiety in his daily life. Such dreams should become less and less frequent.

Kindergarten

Most five-year-olds adjust happily to kindergarten, and this is a fine experience for your youngster to have. It helps accustom him to a group and to routines of regular school in an easy, delightful way. Of course, if your child has gone to nursery school, he has already learned many of these lessons and is not likely to be worried at the idea of being separated from Mother for a few hours of the day. Even without this preparation, however, the five-year-old often wants to report to the kindergarten teacher all by himself, after Mother has taken him to the school. Or it may make him feel very big to go to school the first day with an older friend.

Do not expect him to come home full of tales about what went on at school. The five-year-old, as a rule, has little to say about this. You may have to find out how he is getting on by visiting school once in a while or talking with the teacher.

Most children of this age are better off for a daily rest, and the half-day schedule of the usual kindergarten makes this possible. If your youngster attends school in the morning, he may lie down for a while after his lunch, with a picture book or toy. If he attends the afternoon session, he may have his rest before he eats his lunch.

He may surprise you by dropping off to sleep, but whether he does or not, the rest helps him to take in stride the stimulation and excitement of being with a large group and engaging in lively play.

Social Know How

Along with the many other delightful manifestations of this period, the five-year-old often shows devotion to a younger brother or sister, and plays with the younger child much more amiably than before. He likes best, however, to play with youngsters of his own age, and out of doors where he can be active and vigorous. He is still not fully developed as a social being, however, and while he gets along beautifully with one other child, trouble may develop where there are three. In that case, one is almost certain to be picked on or left out. Junior is not yet old enough to realize that it works both ways: he and Johnnie have a wonderful time today tormenting Sally, but tomorrow the chances are that Johnnie and Sally will gleefully make his life miserable.

On days when an odd number is inescapable, try to make things bearable for the unwanted child, but don't be worried about this behavior. Junior is learning more advanced social attitudes one step at a time. By the time he is seven or eight, he will know how to handle a number of friends and to play with a larger group. You may note how much more cooperative his play has already become with the one child. That is a distinct advance over the self-centered play of the preschool years.

The five-year-old is still far from stable emotionally, despite the great advances he has made in this respect. Don't let the play period stretch out too long. With fatigue, explosions may result that could have been avoided by breaking up the play tactfully, or by suggesting a quiet form of amusement after children have been tearing about for several hours.

Paints, crayons, modeling clay, and cutting out (scissors must still have blunt ends) are favorite indoor sports, and roller skates, scooter, coaster wagon, or sidewalk bicycle can be added to the outdoor fun equipment.

Sex Development

Children of five or six may be interested in exploring each other's bodies and in sex play. Again, this does not mean that your youngster is going to be abnormal. It is part of the natural curiosity about the world he lives in, and when this is satisfied, the child's attentions turn normally to other things. Around six there is also a tendency to masturbation, particularly on the part of boys. Making a child feel wicked or guilty about these things may have a serious effect upon his sex adjustments in adult life. Parents should meet these manifestations calmly, recognizing them as a stage of development and a kind of behavior that will be left behind in due time. The child's attention can be diverted tactfully to other things, but with care to see that the sex curiosity itself is not branded as "bad" in the child's consciousness.

On the other hand, many five-year-olds develop a sense of modesty about their bodies, and cease to run about the house naked as they have done before. These impulses, too, should be respected; they should not be a subject for teasing or speculation.

There is a great deal of interest in babies, but not so much in respect to learning where babies come from. The five-year-old is interested in babies for themselves, and wishes that he had a baby brother or sister, or a baby of his own.

An Allowance Indicated

If he hasn't had an allowance before, the five-year-old should be given money of his own—enough to allow him to make some small purchase of his own choosing each week. But do not withhold the allowance as a punishment. The purpose of the allowance at this early age is to give him a little experience in handling money and a feeling of independence that comes with making his own choices.

Later, he may be taught the advantages of saving to acquire some desired object, but the five-year-old is hardly ready for this.

Going on Six

Sometime during this year between five and six, don't be surprised if your youngster loses some of his wonderful amenability and begins to be contrary now and then. This is not as marked, usually, as in the two-to-three-year-old, but it arises from the same cause—an urge toward independence. Again it is a sign to give him more freedom of choice and freedom of action where you can. In the case of rules that must be observed, hold to them in the same firm, friendly way as before, but look at your rules from time to time to see whether all are as important as you think.

Around six, too, it is expected that your youngster's interests will turn toward the outside world, his playmates, his teacher, instead of being centered in his home and parents as at the age of five. He may find a little girl whom he wishes to marry when he grows up, instead of Mother; or he may dote on his kindergarten teacher.

All of this is natural and desirable. Establishing strong relationships in the outside world is a necessary part of his development. As is usually the case when he reaches out toward some new accomplishment, he may go through a period when he seems not to care very much about his home and his parents. But the deep love is still there. Right now he is bent upon establishing himself as a member of a social order, and few things are more important for his future happiness.

Regular School

And now, at last, your youngster is ready for the final milestone in the progress from infancy—the beginning of regular school. Most children look forward eagerly to this experience. Between five and six there is often interest in figures, and some youngsters teach themselves to read by asking adults to tell them the words in newspaper headlines or storybooks.

Not all children are ready for these experiences at the same age, but the well-adjusted six-year-old is ready for the step into the outside world which school represents. Do not be critical of your youngster's school if he does not become an adept reader or figurer as soon as he enters first grade. Up-to-date teachers try to make the introduction to regular school a happy one. They know that when youngsters have reached the point where they are ready to learn to read, write, and figure, they will attack these skills purposefully. Urging them upon a child who is not yet ready for them, on the other hand, accomplishes little except to make the child unhappy and to make school hateful to him.

Hence, if the first school reports are more concerned with progress in social attitudes and adaptation to school routines than they are with progress in reading and writing, this is as it should be. The whole emphasis of modern education is upon helping the child to develop as a whole, well-rounded individual. We have known parents who were disconcerted to have a teacher report that their child was happy in school. "But what about reading and writing?" they ask. "Isn't that what we send children to school for—to learn, not just to be happy?"

The teacher knows that a happy child is in the best frame of mind for learning. It will be such a painless process for him that his parents may not even know it is going on. We knew a "happy" first-grader whose parents entered him in first grade a second year at another school because they didn't think he had learned anything during his first year. Their faces turned red when the report came that their child was ready to do excellent work in the second grade!

Parents can help in their child's development by continually widening the opportunities to explore, to work with new materials and learn new skills, and by granting further independence as the youngster arrives at new levels of maturity.

Portrait of a five-year-old

Early childhood is almost over when a child is five. Here is a self-reliant young individual who enjoys groups. Although all "fives" differ from each other, they have traits in common, as research shows, and it is helpful to parents to know what to expect.

Can dress himself if he wants to and if his clothes are put out for him.

Skillful tricycle rider. Climbs with sureness. Tries bike riding and roller skating. Good at acrobatics.

Two play best together. If there are three, two children are apt to gang up on one.

Usually adjusts easily to kindergarten. May want Mother to take him to school for the first few days.

Sand box, swing, climbing apparatus, and large blocks are popular outdoor equipment.

Plays well in group, usually on own project. Adult needed as distant patrolman, rather than close supervisor.

Likes to build with blocks. Girls make dollhouses; boys, quarters for fire engines, airplanes, tanks, bridges, tunnels.

Likes to paint, draw, color, paste. Has become definitely right- or left-handed.

Washes face and hands before meals if reminded, and helps with bath. Can't yet draw bath because of hot-water danger.

Likes to finish what he's started. Less dawdling.

Wants to please and help Mother—the preferred parent. Usually asks her permission before acting.

Positive and argumentative. If pushed too far, may become angry and call names. Cries if scolded sharply.

Feeds self slowly but skillfully. Among favorite foods are: meat, potatoes, raw vegetables, milk, and fruit.

Beginning to understand time words. Interested in clock and calendar. Knows days of the week.

Likes to go on expeditions with Father, helping Father with household repairs.

Enjoys visiting his grandparents, hearing their stories about his own parents' childhood.

Likes Sunday school (though it's too much to expect him to sit through regular church services).

Gets along well with older and younger brothers and sisters, but may tease young ones if together too long.

Both boys and girls interested in playing with dolls. Both express desire to have own babies.

Becoming bashful about letting others see him undressed. Decrease in sex play.

Talks a lot and clearly. Can tell a story, answer the telephone, and take a message.

Likes to play records, dance, listen to radio and TV. Some can pick out tune on piano.

Likes to play simple counting and alphabet games. Knows penny, nickel, dime.

Enjoys having parents read to him. Memory enables him to "read" to younger brothers and sisters.

Will usually cooperate in plan to give up thumb sucking. But nail biting, nose picking are common.

Afraid of thunder, and sirens at night. Afraid that Mother will go away and not return, or not be there if he awakens.

Frequent dreams and nightmares. Animal dreams predominate. May awaken screaming.

Comforting and reassuring the child will help him conquer fears. Logical arguments and ridicule won't help.

CHAPTER SEVENTEEN

Toy guide

This list of toys for children from one month to six years has been planned as an intelligent parents' guide to toy selection, not as an arbitrary "must" or the final word on what your children will like. Some children have special aptitudes and highly developed interests; and no age classification can be perfect. When selecting toys, use this guide plus a consideration of the individual child and his special interests.

The newcomer: one month to one year. The infant examines the world into which he has come with his eyes, ears, fingers, and mouth.

Mobile.
Colored toys to attach to crib.
Exercise toys.
Strung disks, measuring spoons.
Brightly colored plastic rattles, animals, suction-cup rattles.
Washable rag dolls.
Soft stuffed animals.
Rocking-chair horse.
Small bell with handle.
Musical toys.
Baby swing.
Teething toys.
For the bath: floating toys.
Roly-poly.
Rubber animals.
Unbreakable water ball.
Toys to push.
Soft plush or plastic ball.

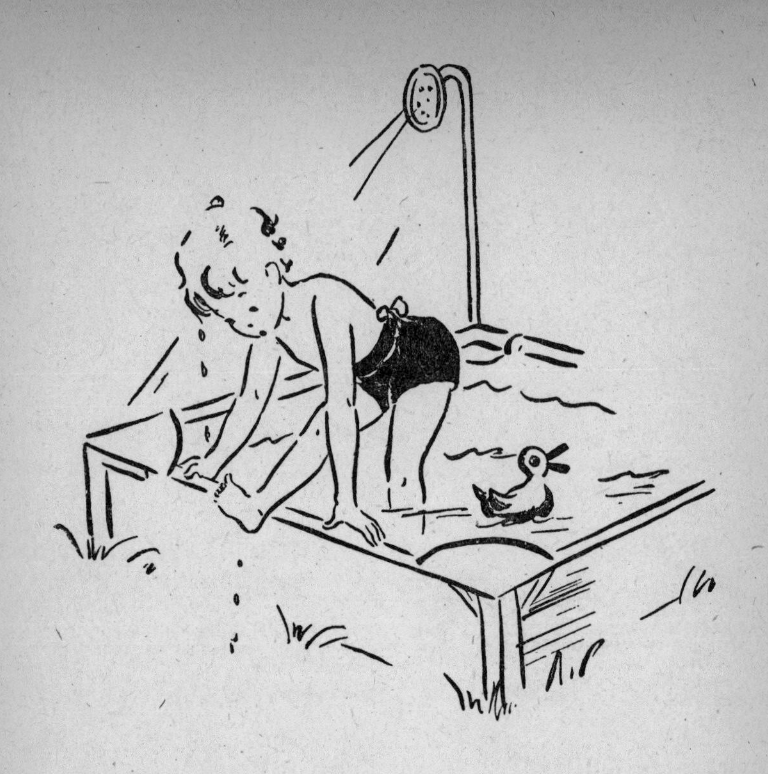

The explorer: one to two years. The world in all its mystery is opening up to the child who can get around by himself. This is the age when parental patience must be at its highest and standards of neatness in the home most elastic, for the child wants to pick up, drop, carry, put into something, or take out of something every single object he can see or reach.

Pull-and-push toys.
Small truck to ride on, wheelbarrow, wagon.
Cart of building blocks.
Small rocking horse.
Large wooden or plastic beads.
Unbreakable dishes, apron.
Easy wood puzzles especially designed for this age.
Small chair he can carry.
Hammering, put-together trains and boats toy.
Nest of blocks.
Tables and chairs.
Luggage.

The man of action: two to four years. The child changes during these years in a fascinating way from a baby to a real person. Physical, social, and intellectual growth are so great that appropriate toys exist almost without number. He is gaining in muscular strength.

Small-size tricycle.
Outdoor swing, teeter-totter, sandbox, wading pool.
Sand toys.
Sled.
A girl or boy doll.
Small wagon to pull.
Doll buggy.
Miniature cleaning set, cooking set, garden tools, snow shovel.
Toy instruments: drum, xylophone, piano, cymbals.
Music box.
Finger paints.
Crayons.
Building blocks.
Clay for modeling.
Easel for painting.
Books.
Toy telephone.
Records.

The member of society: four to six. The four-year-old is beginning to assume responsibilities for himself as a member of society, as a member of a family, and as a person. As he finds his place in a community of children, he begins to need the constant shelter and companionship of his home somewhat less, although the security it represents must always remain if he is to find the freedom and courage necessary to venture away from home. Dolls help supply a tie to the family, as do cooking and sewing equipment.

Dollhouse.
Playhouse.
Balls.
Beanbags, magnetic darts, jump ropes.
Colored paper and scissors.
Books, records, and paints.
A tool set, workbench.
Building blocks—bricks, cylinders, arches, and pillars.
Wooden people to accompany block buildings.
Fleet of boats.
Wood freight train.
Jigsaw puzzles.
Pocketbook, bank, or cash register.
Doctor's set, toy store.
Sturdy metal coasting wagon.
Scooter.
Hook-and-ladder fire truck.
Baby doll and layette.
Bassinet.
Ironing board and electric iron.
Metal cabinet stove.
Police, fireman, nurse—play outfits.
Barn and farmyard animals.
Matching games, objects, animals, flowers, birds.
Simple card games.
Hanging blackboard.
Automobile in which to ride.
Picnic basket.
Swing, bars, ladder, slide.

CHAPTER EIGHTEEN

The health care of the young child

By Dorothy V. Whipple, M.D.
Member of the American Academy of Pediatrics
Formerly with the United States Children's Bureau

You certainly want to protect your child against every illness you possibly can. Medical science has made great strides in the past few decades and is better prepared to help you than ever before. Many diseases which in years past have taken a heavy toll of infants' lives are now almost wiped out. Others, though not preventable as yet, can be cured once they do strike. There are still, of course, some diseases which doctors do not know how to prevent or how to cure. But you will want to take advantage of all the knowledge we do have to keep your baby in the best of health. Up-to-date daily care will protect your child from many of the ills that worried your grandmother.

General Measures

We know a great deal about nutrition. Your doctor gives you instructions about what and how to feed your children to avoid diseases due to inadequate or poorly selected food. Throughout the pages of this book are suggestions about proper food and diet for babies and little children. No child these days need suffer from rickets or scurvy or pellagra or beriberi (each one due to a lack of a special vitamin). By the proper preparation and storage of food you can avoid many digestive disturbances. We understand, today, about bacteria, how they get into food, and what harm they can do. With this knowledge you can protect your baby. The details of formula making, Chapter Five, page 45, are important to guard against harmful bacteria in the baby's food.

We also know about the danger to babies from minor infections. A simple cold in an adult may cause a serious respiratory illness in a baby. Hence the importance of keeping your baby away from anyone with a cold.

Sunshine, fresh air, cleanliness, play, and exercise all help to keep your baby healthy. Throughout the pages of this book you will find many suggestions concerning these things.

Immunization Needs

During a baby's first year he gets a number of shots to protect him against various diseases. The schedule will vary according to your doctor's planning. New vaccines are appearing; your doctor or local public health service can keep you up-to-date.

Between one and two months your baby will probably be given his first D-P-T inoculation, a combination against diphtheria, pertussis (whooping cough) and tetanus (lockjaw). A month later he will get a second shot, and a third will follow the next month. A booster shot is generally given six months to a year later.

Polio inoculation (with the Salk vaccine) can be combined today with the D-P-T vaccines. If it is taken separately by injection, the first of the series of shots should be given between six weeks and three months. Each inoculation protects against all three types of polio. Second and third shots are given at six-week intervals and a fourth after six months. Your doctor may recommend additional boosters under special circumstances such as an epidemic or travel.

If oral polio vaccine is given, approximately the same schedule is followed. However, each dose is effective for only one type of polio until the fourth, which is a combination for all three types.

Smallpox vaccination may be given at any time during a baby's first year, and should be repeated routinely every four years.

Typhoid vaccination is rarely given unless drinking water is contaminated, or typhoid is a definite possibility for some other reason—if you plan to travel outside the United States, for example. There are three shots, given at intervals of one to four weeks.

Periodic Health Checkups

Doctors generally recommend the following regimen for family health examinations:

Birth to 6 months.........monthly
6 months to 1 year........bi-monthly
1 to 2 years..............tri-yearly
2 to 5 years..............semi-yearly
After 5 years............yearly

Teeth: Take your child to the dentist at the age of three and then about every six months.

Eyes: If the baby's eyes continue to cross after three months of age, consult an eye doctor. Treatment for defective vision should be started early. Have your child's vision checked by an eye doctor before he starts school.

Ears: If your baby does not show normal reaction to sound, consult a specialist. Corrective measures, including use of a hearing aid, may be started under six months of age. Early treatment of deafness is important for the development of speech.

Periodic school tests for hearing and vision are customary; some programs include more thorough examinations. The school recommends that children see a doctor about special health problems. Many conditions caught early can be cleared up easily.

Family Health Record

An up-to-date health and medical history of each member of the family can be invaluable for current and future use.

Record birth information, including any delivery complications, anesthesia used; names of all doctors; illnesses and treatment, including antibiotics; immunizations with dates; reactions to injections and medicines; allergies; infections; injuries; surgery; hospitalization; X-rays (including dental); visual or other impairment; blood type.

Good Health Routines

Set up regular hours for meals and bedtime. Allow for outdoor play daily. Watch for over-tiredness, over-heating, chilling.

Keep children away from sick people. Avoid taking young children into crowds.

Be sure drinking water is safe, at home and on trips. Boil all drinking water for infants. Keep formula refrigerated.

Make the daily bath a pleasant habit by allowing time for relaxation and play.

Teach your child to:

Observe local ordinances for community health protection.

Wash hands before meals and after using the toilet.

Brush teeth and rinse mouth after eating, especially sweets.

Cover mouth and nose when coughing or sneezing; dispose of used tissues.

Use only his own toilet articles—towels, toothbrush, comb.

Good Safety Habits

Teach safety—not timidity. Try not to overprotect your child. Teach skills and abilities that will encourage self-confidence. In emergencies, try to set the good example of cool-headedness.

Create a safe environment. Correct dangerous conditions in your home, yard and children's play places. Here are a few musts:

Keep a first-aid book handy. (See page 225.)

Never leave a young child alone in the house or in a room with a lighted stove.

Keep medicines in high cabinet, locked if necessary.

Store cleaning fluid, bleach, insecticides, sharp instruments, matches, and other dangerous objects out of reach or locked away.

Dispose of polyethylene plastic bags.

Teach traffic rules, and the safest home-school route.

Never leave young children alone in a parked car. Provide a car bed or car seat for the baby or toddler. A child over three is safest wearing a safety belt. Equip your car with safety door locks.

Your Medicine Chest

One of the most frequently used pieces of bathroom furniture is the indispensable medicine chest. Yet most of us pay very little attention to it. We can find the regularly used razor or the nightly cold cream fast enough, but in an emergency we are lost. Precious time is wasted poking into corners or having to make a quick trip to the drugstore to get something we had "meant to buy but forgot." A well-stocked medicine chest is, therefore, essential. It is a good idea, too, to have a first-aid chart and a poison reference chart fastened to the back of your medicine cabinet door.

Most poisonings are from common drugs and household preparations; keep such items out of reach of small children, in locked cabinets if child can climb. Never use leftover medicines for another illness before checking with your doctor. Label every box and bottle clearly, and always read the label before taking or giving any medicine.

Fortunately, most home ailments and injuries are minor and can be treated at home. Below is a handy checklist of supplies. But don't try to treat a serious illness or injury. Call your doctor!

For First Aid Treatment. Adhesive gauze pads • Adhesive tape, 1" • Antiseptic • Plastic bandages • Sterile absorbent cotton • Sterile cotton swabs • Sterile gauze pads, 2" x 2", 3" x 3" • Sterile gauze rolls, 2", 3" • Universal antidote for poisoning.

Aids to Comfort and Recovery. Air atomizer • Disinfectant (hospital approved) • Electric heating pad, ice bag • Hot water bottle, syringe • Pain relief remedy • Safety pins • Scissors (blunt tipped) • Thermometer, oral, rectal • Tweezers • Vaporizer, inhalant, spray vaporizer.

Other Cabinet Necessities. Burn remedy* • Cold, cough remedies, chest rub* • Dentifrice • Diarrhea remedy* • Eye cup • Fever remedy* • Indigestion remedy* • Laxative (mild)* • Lip balm • Mouth wash • Nausea, motion sickness remedy* • Nose, throat medication* • Petroleum jelly • Rubbing alcohol.

* For children, what your doctor orders

Common Communicable Diseases

DISEASE	SYMPTOMS	INCUBATION PERIOD
MEASLES	Fever; runny eyes; eruption in mouth followed by rash on face and body.	From 7 to 14 days before onset of fever (rash appears as late as 7 days after fever).
GERMAN MEASLES	Slight fever, sore throat or cold symptoms may precede rash; glands in neck swollen.	Usually about 18 days, varies plus or minus 6 days.
CHICKEN POX	Successive crops of pimples or blisters, more on trunk than limbs and face; slight fever.	From 14 to 16 days, occasionally as long as 21 days.
WHOOPING COUGH (Pertussis)	Tight, dry cough that becomes steadily worse for 2 weeks until "whooping," noise of in-rushing breath, begins. Vomiting often follows coughing spasms.	From 5 to 10 days; occasionally as long as 21 days.
MUMPS	Fever; swelling of the salivary glands in the cheeks and under the tongue. Many cases are so mild as to go unrecognized, yet they spread infection.	From 12 to 28 days, usually 18 days.
STREP THROAT (including Scarlet Fever)	Sore, inflamed throat; fever; nausea; followed (in the case of scarlet fever) in a day or two by a red rash on the warm moist parts of body, possibly spreading over whole body and sides of face, but mouth region stays pale.	From 2 to 5 days.
DIPHTHERIA	Inflammation of the tonsils, throat and nose with grayish-white patches; fever.	Usually 2 to 6 days.
INFLUENZA	Sudden onset; fever; aching limbs and back; runny nose; sore throat; cough.	Usually 1 to 3 days.
POLIO (Infantile Paralysis)	Fever; pain on bending neck downward to chest; headache; vomiting. Later, muscle groups may be weakened and possibly paralyzed.	Usually 7 to 14 days, but may be less.

COMMUNICABILITY	HOME CARE
Most contagious for 4 days preceding rash and first 5 days of rash.	Isolation. Follow doctor's instructions carefully. Complications can be serious.
For 4 days before and 5 days after rash appears.	Isolation. Not serious. (But may cause defects in baby if mother has the disease in first three months of pregnancy.)
Highly infectious for 7 days, beginning the day before rash appears.	Isolation. Calamine lotion or a paste of baking soda and water to relieve itching. Trim fingernails short.
From appearance of cold symptoms for at least 4 weeks. Greatest before onset of whooping.	Isolation. Avoid sudden temperature changes that bring on coughing. Holding forehead and abdomen during coughing spasms helps prevent vomiting. Needs careful supervision of doctor throughout illness.
From a few days before fever until swelling of the glands disappears.	Isolation. Cold or hot applications may ease pain.
Apparently runs the course of a strep throat attack, from first appearance of symptoms until complete recovery; scarlet fever can be caught from someone with strep throat who has no scarlet fever symptoms.	Isolation in bed for rest; guard against chilling. Needs prompt and careful supervision of doctor to shorten illness and greatly lessen chances of complications.
Until bacilli disappear completely (as shown by tests), usually in 2 weeks or less, rarely more than 4 weeks.	Isolation. Prompt doctor's attention. Strict bed rest. Soft or liquid foods.
Probably briefly before onset and up to 1 week thereafter.	Bed rest. Avoid chilling. Consult doctor.
Presumably for several days before onset of symptoms and for approximately 5 days afterwards.	Isolation. Prompt and continued doctor's care is imperative. (Hospitalization is common.)

When Baby Is Sick

Babies, like adults, usually give some warning signals before real illness strikes, and much fear and worry can be avoided if you learn to recognize these symptoms. Every baby is subject to an occasional sneeze or cough, brief cranky spell, spitting up directly after a feeding, or even an extra bowel movement or two. These things come within the bounds of normal behavior in the first months and year of life and are no cause for concern. A marked change—with or without fever—in your baby's normal behavior or appearance, as indicated by the guide below, means that your doctor should be consulted promptly.

When you first suspect illness, write down your observations as accurately as possible. This will aid your doctor in his diagnosis. Never dose the baby yourself with laxatives, aspirin, ear or nose drops, nor give any medicine or treatment that has not been prescribed by your physician for this illness and for this particular case. These are the signs and symptoms to report to your doctor:

General Behavior. Unusually quiet, irritable, or drowsy.

Appetite. More than one feeding refused.

Vomiting. All or a large part of a feeding vomited, vomiting between feedings, or vomiting forcefully as opposed to the usual spitting up.

Bowel Movements and Urine. Sudden increase or decrease in number of stools. Stools unusual in color, odor or consistency. Decrease or change in urine.

Fever. Rectal temperature 101 degrees or above.

Color. Unusually flushed or pale complexion.

Skin. Dry or hot skin. Excess perspiration. Rash.

Breathing. Hoarseness, continued sneezing or coughing. Labored or unusually noisy or rapid or slow breathing. Discharge from nose.

Eyes. Red, irritated or especially sensitive to light.

Bodily Movement. Convulsions—pronounced twitching or shaking of the body. Stiffness or immobility in any part of the body.

Pain. Sharp screaming, head-rolling, or ear-rubbing.

Nursing Techniques

Taking the Temperature. Hold the upper end of a clean rectal thermometer between thumb and fingers. Shake it with sharp downward snaps of the wrist until the silvery or colored mercury is below the 97 degree mark. Do this over a bed or pillow so the thermometer will not be broken if it slips out of your hand. Apply a dab of petroleum jelly or cold cream to the bulb end of the thermometer for easy insertion. Place the baby across your knees, buttocks up. Unpin his diaper but leave it in place to protect your lap.

Separate his buttocks with one hand and gently insert the thermometer about an inch into the rectum. It will go in easily if you hold it lightly. Support the baby with one hand and hold the thermometer loosely in place with the other. One minute will give a fairly close reading by rectum.

Gently pull the thermometer out and put it safely aside. Re-diaper the baby and put him in his crib.

Wipe off the thermometer with tissue. In a good light, slowly rotate the barrel until you see the mercury. Read the temperature where the mercury column ends. Don't worry about accuracy to a small fraction of a degree. Wash the thermometer with soap and warm (not hot) water before putting it away.

Take the temperature about every four hours and keep a written record.

Giving Medicine. Most infants won't object to the pleasant taste of baby aspirin. Your doctor will tell you the exact amount of aspirin in liquid or tablet form that is right for your baby's age.

You can give liquid aspirin directly from a dropper. Crush tablets in a little water or juice and give from a spoon. It is advisable to hold the baby upright when you give any medicine. Push down on the chin and put the spoon or dropper well into his mouth. If he spits some back, scoop it up with the spoon and give it to him again. If he vomits it sometime afterwards, let your doctor know. He may want you to give it again or he may try a different kind of medicine.

Today, antibiotics are given for many illnesses, with dosage carefully calculated for the baby's age and weight. The medicines usually come with marked droppers to help you give the exact amount ordered. Children under three react so quickly to drugs that you may be tempted to stop the medicine when you see a rapid improvement. But unless your doctor directs you otherwise, give all the antibiotic he has prescribed.

Generally, all medicine should be given from a spoon or dropper. If you put it in a bottle with formula or juice, you run the risk that some may stick to the sides, or that the baby will not finish his bottle.

For a baby, tablets must be mashed and can be mixed with a spoonful of liquid or strained fruit. Unpleasant tasting medicines can be disguised in fruit, sugar and water, honey or syrup. Have the medicine ready before you take up the baby, and slip it into his mouth in a matter-of-fact way, without preliminaries.

Giving Fluids. You've probably heard a nurse or doctor say, "Force fluids." This is a medical term and is not meant to be taken literally; it simply means that you should encourage your baby to take as much fluid as possible. Offer boiled, cooled water or diluted juice as often as once an hour when he is awake, and keep a record of how much he takes.

If your baby is vomiting, withhold liquids for half an hour, then offer a small amount and increase, gradually, if he can keep it down. Liquids replace body fluids lost in fever.

With vomiting or diarrhea, don't give the baby his regular formula until you talk to your doctor. He may suggest that you dilute the milk or withhold it entirely for a while.

If you are breast feeding, there is usually no need to stop. Breast milk is more easily digested than formula, and the cuddling and pleasure associated with feeding are comforting to a sick baby. If your baby wants less breast milk than usual, you can maintain your supply by manually expressing the milk remaining after each feeding or using a breast pump.

Giving a Sponge-off. To help lower an elevated temperature, a tepid wet rub may be prescribed. You can do this quickly and easily, using a bowl of lukewarm water and a small washcloth.

Undress the baby in a warm room without drafts. Place him in the center of a bath towel and cover him with a sheet or light blanket. Expose one part of his body at a time—a leg, an arm, the back, the chest—and rub gently with the wet washcloth for a minute or two; then cover this part before proceeding.

Dress him in something that covers his entire body—as a drawstring nightgown or pajamas. If the room is evenly heated at ordinary room temperature (68 to 70 degrees) he'll need no more than a lightweight blanket, perhaps only a sheet.

Giving an Enema. Sometimes an enema is prescribed by the doctor to relieve constipation or to bring down a high temperature. Unless the doctor prescribes a special solution, use warm water (body temperature) in a small bulb syringe—a half-cup of water for a small infant, a cupful for a one-year-old. Lubricate the tip of the syringe with petroleum jelly. Keep a potty or extra diapers close at hand.

Put the baby on a waterproof sheet covered with an absorbent pad across your knees or on a bed. Squeeze the syringe slowly until the air is expelled and you see the first drops of water drip from the tip.

Keeping the same pressure on the syringe, so as to prevent air from entering it, separate the baby's buttocks and gently insert the tip about one inch into the rectum. Continue to squeeze the bulb slowly until it is empty. Keep the syringe tightly compressed until after it's removed, so the water won't be sucked back.

For best results, keep the baby's buttocks pressed together for a few minutes. Don't worry if all the water does not come out with the first bowel movement; some may be absorbed and the rest will be expelled later.

General Comfort. Keep your baby as quiet as possible during an illness and away from the family and visitors. Don't bother him with unnecessary attention when he is relaxed or drowsy. Encourage rest by darkening the room, talking soothingly to him when he requires attention. If he is fretful and cranky, he may be soothed if you hold and rock him gently in a rocking chair. Try not to let your face, voice or actions show your worry. Calm, pleasant mothering is "good medicine."

Don't worry about schedules. Let your baby sleep and eat as much as he likes. Never urge him to eat.

If coughing and cold symptoms are part of your child's illness, use a spray, or a vaporizer with soothing medication or plain water to moisturize the air in his room. Always keep equipment out of Baby's reach, and where no one will trip over it. Direct the column of steam away from the crib. Keep windows and doors closed and put the baby to sleep on his stomach to help the mucus drain. Your doctor may recommend a mild medicament as a chest rub, and a soft-tip ear syringe to suck mucus from the nose.

After the baby's temperature has returned to normal and his other symptoms have disappeared, keep him in the house for two days, as his resistance to germs will be temporarily lowered.

Three-month Colic

A healthy infant who has intense spells of crying may have colic—sharp intestinal pain. Consult your doctor. To lessen swallowed air, hold Baby nearly upright to feed, and burp him well. Tension is a common cause; he may find relief in a calmer life, a pacifier, rocking, lying on his stomach over a warm, well-wrapped hot-water bottle. Colic rarely occurs after three months.

In Case of Emergency

Knowing how to prevent and handle common home accidents should be a part of every mother's liberal education. For no matter how much safety proofing you do, and how watchful you are, there are bound to be a few emergencies—small ones most of the time, big ones occasionally. If you know what to do in such situations, your panicky feeling diminishes. In the case of a serious accident, you must assume responsibility until a doctor is reached. In a minor accident, your child will feel better sooner if you are calm and sure in your administrations. In all cases of accidents, communicate with a doctor. The following guide will help until you can obtain medical aid.

LIST EMERGENCY PHONE NUMBERS HERE
DOCTOR ....
HOSPITAL ....
PHARMACIST ....
POISON CONTROL CENTER ....

Abdominal Pain. Call the doctor promptly. Keep child lying down and quiet. Never give laxative, enema or medication except on doctor's order.

Animal Bites. Wash wound with strong soap under running water. Immediately contact a doctor, the police and a veterinarian. If possible, confine the animal for rabies testing. Never kill the animal unless absolutely necessary in order to protect other people from being bitten.

Asphyxiation. Ventilate the chamber before attempting rescue. Danger of explosion or asphyxia of the rescuer are otherwise great. If victim is unconscious, administer artificial respiration (see next page) when in fresh air. Call police emergency for oxygen.

Artificial Respiration. See illustrated Mouth-to-Mouth Rescue Breathing on following page. Use as first aid in case of drowning, electric shock, gas poisoning, drug poisoning, compression of chest, choking and strangling, partial obstruction of breathing passages.

Bleeding. All major or deep wounds require prompt medical attention. When a cut or laceration is bleeding profusely, apply direct pressure on it with a sterile pad or clean cloth. The bare hand may be used temporarily to stem a major blood loss until a suitable piece of cloth is obtained. When bleeding is controlled, additional layers of cloth can be applied over the wound and bandaged firmly in place. If bleeding occurs in an extremity, the part should be elevated. Tourniquets should almost never be attempted—only as a last resort when severe bleeding in an extremity threatens life. Nosebleeds in children are rarely serious. The best measure is to

Mouth-to-mouth Rescue Breathing

Place child on back. Insert middle finger of one hand to clear mouth and hold tongue forward. Turn child over—face and head down. With finger holding tongue, pat back with free hand to expel foreign matter in air passage.

Place child on back again. Using middle finger of both hands, lift lower jaw from beneath so that it juts out.

Holding jaw in position with one hand, cover the child's mouth and nose with your mouth, sealing them in as well as possible. Breathe into child with a smooth steady action until chest rises. Use free hand to apply moderate pressure to abdomen between navel and ribs to keep stomach from filling with air. When lungs are inflated, free mouth and nose, allowing lungs to empty. Repeat—about 20 shallow breaths per minute—until help comes or breathing returns to normal.

keep the child quiet with his head thrown back, if sitting, or head and shoulders raised, if lying down. The nose should not be blown. Pinching the nostrils together or application of cold wet towels sometimes helps. Bleeding from the nose or mouth as a result of injury elsewhere requires immediate medical attention. If breathing is difficult, the head and shoulders should be raised.

Blisters. Protect against breaking. If blister is large, have physician open it. Otherwise, clean with soap and water, then puncture edge with sterilized needle. Carefully force fluid out, cover with sterile gauze pad. (This should not be done for blisters caused by burns.)

Blood Poisoning. The telltale signs are red streaks radiating from a wound, usually accompanied by chills and fever. This is an extremely serious condition which no home "first aid" treatment can help. Get immediate medical aid.

Boils. Do not squeeze. Protect from pressure. Relieve pain with wet compresses of Epsom salt solution—one tablespoon to a pint of warm water. (Do not apply to face except under medical direction.) Have doctor open. If boil breaks, wipe pus with sterile pad wet with rubbing alcohol, wiping from normal skin toward the boil. Then apply sterile dressing.

Burns. For a small, minor burn, cold clean water reduces pain and swelling. For bad burns over the size of a half-dollar, apply thick dry sterile dressing and see a doctor at once. If blisters appear, do not rupture. Treat a badly burned person for shock (see page 232) until medical aid arrives.

Sunburn: To relieve pain, use a sunburn remedy recommended by your doctor, or cold cream, plain salad oil or shortening (not butter or margarine). Keep out of sun until healed. Severe cases or blistering require medical care.

Chemical Burns: Immediately wash the chemical from the skin or eyes with large quantities of water. Check label of container to see if there are first aid directions. If not, give first aid to skin as for similar heat burn. For eyes, get *immediate* medical aid.

Choking. Turn child upside down and smack him between the shoulder blades. Encourage coughing if possible. If you know object swallowed was sharp, and if it doesn't dislodge, or if it interferes with breathing, rush child to the nearest hospital or summon the police or fire department. If breathing falters or stops, begin mouth-to-mouth rescue breathing illustrated on page 226.

Concussion. Contact the doctor immediately in case of any of the following symptoms resulting from a fall or blow on the head: temporary blackout; grogginess; headache; vomiting; bleeding from nose, ears or mouth; heavy or labored breathing; continued paleness or flush or loss of appetite. Keep injured person very quiet, comfortably warm, and in a horizontal position. Raise head and shoulders if face is flushed; use no pillow if face is pale. Give no stimulants.

Convulsions. (Spasms and twitching of the body in various degrees, sometimes with loss of consciousness.) Convulsions usually stop in a short time without treatment, but medical attention is important to diagnose the cause. Watch to prevent self-harm. Place a blunt or padded object between teeth. If fever is high, give wet rubs until doctor arrives.

Crushing Injuries. Free the injured person by lifting the weight from his body. Do not drag him free if he is pinned fast. Wait for help. Send for medical aid at once. Try to stop bleeding and prevent shock (see pages 225 and 232). If injury is to trunk of the body do not attempt to move him. If a chest injury is involved, place many layers of dressing material against the wound, in case air is passing through it. If breathing falters, use mouth-to-mouth rescue breathing (see page 226). Keep person warm. If an arm or leg has been injured and the patient must be moved, apply a firm, well-padded splint, not tied too tightly. Do not apply heat in any form. Minor mishaps can be treated by applying cold compresses to reduce swelling but if pain persists or swelling is severe, have a doctor examine the injury.

Cuts and Lacerations. Immediately clean all minor cuts with soap and warm water. Apply a sterile gauze dressing and bandage loosely. Do not use iodine. Consult your doctor about use of antiseptic. Do not attempt to remove foreign bodies such as dirt, glass or metal particles unless they work off easily during cleansing, but refer injured person to a physician. Change the bandage often enough to keep it clean and dry. Major and deep wounds require prompt medical attention. Limit first aid to covering the wound with a sterile dressing and applying pressure to stop bleeding (page 225).

Dislocations. Do not attempt to move the part affected. Keep it immobile, seek medical help. If dislocation is in shoulder and patient must be moved to medical help, an arm sling may be used to prevent jolts. An ice bag on the area reduces pain and swelling.

Drowning. See Mouth-to-Mouth Rescue Breathing, illustrated on page 226.

Earache. Call the doctor. Prompt medical attention is particularly important when there is any fever. Pain may be relieved meanwhile by applying heat or cold, whichever seems most helpful. If the ear discharges, plug it with a loose wad of sterile absorbent cotton, so that the pus will be absorbed. Never use ear drops or other medications unless advised by physician.

Electric Shock. Don't touch the person or his clothing until contact with the electricity is broken. If indoors, turn off master switch. You may pull him away from the electrical source, using a dry rope, dry clothing or other nonconductor looped over his foot or hand, making sure your hands are dry and you are standing on a dry surface, or push the source of electric current away from him with a dry stick or other long dry object that is a nonconductor. If outdoors, danger to the rescuer is much greater. Phone police, fire department or power company to have current shut off. See that a doctor and ambulance are summoned. When electric contact is broken, start artificial respiration.

Foreign Bodies. ***In the Ear:*** The object should be removed as soon as possible by a doctor. Don't try to remove it yourself. Probing about in the ear can have serious results. If an insect has entered the ear, fill the ear canal gradually with warm mineral oil, baby oil, olive oil or even clear water. Keep the patient lying on the opposite side for a few minutes so that the oil can remain in the ear, then turn so that the oil can run out. If the drowned insect does not come out with the oil, then consult a doctor immediately.

In the Eye: Don't rub the eye. Inspect inner eyelid by pulling lid down, out and back over a swab or matchstick or similar object while child looks down. If speck is seen on inner surface of lid, remove with tip of clean handkerchief or gauze. If speck is seen on eyeball and cannot be flushed away by blinking and tearing, flush with a solution of boric acid in warm water. If irritation continues, speck remains or cannot be found, see a doctor.

In the Nose: Have child blow his nose, or make him sneeze by tickling the other nostril or using pepper. This will often expel the object. (Caution: Don't ask him to blow his nose if he is so young that he sniffs before blowing.) Don't try to remove the object yourself. Have a doctor remove it.

In the Stomach: Never give a laxative to expel a foreign body from the stomach. Round and smooth objects are generally passed out in bowel movements without difficulty. Examine the stools for a few days. If doubt remains or if there is vomiting or pain, call a doctor. If sharp objects like a straight pin, an open safety pin or a tack are swallowed, don't wait. Call a doctor at once.

In the Throat: See Choking, page 227.

Fractures. First aid should be directed to preventing further injury, and no more. If medical aid is immediately available, no splinting or moving of the injured part of the person should be attempted. Keep broken ends and adjacent joints immobile; give first aid for shock. Apply dressing to any open wounds; control bleeding as directed under Bleeding. Do not push protruding bone back. For pain and swelling, apply ice bag. Do not move injured person until suspected fracture site has been splinted.

Frostbite. Do not rub affected area. Apply firm pressure of warm hand, cover with woolen material and provide extra heavy covering for person. Bring indoors as soon as possible and give warm drink. Immerse frostbitten area in water at body temperature. Avoid excessive heat. If fingers or toes are involved, encourage motion after rewarmed.

Heat Exhaustion. Symptoms may be mild or severe—including fatigue, headache, nausea, profuse perspiration, pale and clammy skin. Temperature is about normal. Have child lie down. Give salt water (half teaspoon salt to half glass of water) when it can be tolerated. If case is severe, call doctor. In case of cramps, press area firmly and apply warm wet towels.

Heat Stroke. Medical care is urgently needed. Symptoms are extremely high temperature, nausea, dizziness, headache, dry mouth, hot dry skin, rapid pulse and possibly unconsciousness. While awaiting doctor put the person in a cool place, on his back, raising his head and shoulders slightly. Remove clothing. If fully conscious, give small doses of salt solution (see Heat Exhaustion, above). Give no stimulants.

Insect Bites and Stings. ***Bee, wasp, yellow jacket:*** If stinger is visible, remove it with tweezers. Apply ice or icewater to sting. In case of multiple stings, call doctor immediately. Relief for stings and other insect bites is also obtained from a paste of baking soda and cold cream, a compress of half-strength ammonia, or calamine lotion.

Ticks: Apply heavy oil to suffocate tick, then remove carefully. Wash area well.

Scorpion, black widow spider and tarantula: Obtain medical help. If sting or bite is on finger or toe, apply a tight constricting band at base of digit and leave for five minutes. Keep area cold with ice packs for several hours and in a position lower than rest of body if possible.

Poisoning and Overdoses. Do not delay first aid. Have someone else phone immediately for medical aid.

- *Do not induce vomiting for the following:* acids, ammonia, cleaning fluids, gasoline, insect sprays, kerosene, liquid polish, lye, solvents, washing soda—or after first five minutes of strychnine poisoning.

- *Induce vomiting immediately*—if the patient is conscious—for other poisoning and for overdoses of medicines, laxatives or drugs. Give fluids in large amounts—water or milk are usually handiest. Several teaspoons of baking soda per half glass of water should help. If fluid is not available, lay child across your lap, face down, with head lower than hips to prevent vomited material from entering windpipe. Then touch back of throat with finger or spoon to induce vomiting. (Continued on next page.)

• *In all cases,* if antidote is given on container of substance swallowed, follow directions there. Otherwise preserve container for contents information on label and get medical advice on antidote. It is advisable for every home to have one or more of the following: a poison antidote chart or book available from the Red Cross and various other organizations; the phone number of the nearest poison control center (hundreds of cities now have these centers which supply emergency instruction day and night); phone number of nearest hospital.

Poison Ivy, Oak and Sumac. After coming into contact with the plant, the exposed areas of the skin should be washed as soon as possible, using plenty of hot water and soap. Apply a thick lather several times but do not scrub. Rinse in clear water, dry, then pat on rubbing alcohol. If rash appears, wash the area thoroughly with soap and water and sponge with rubbing alcohol. A solution such as calamine lotion can be used to relieve itching. If the rash covers an extensive area, see the doctor.

Shock. While awaiting the arrival of a physician, place person on his back, loosen all clothing and cover according to general comfort at the prevailing temperature—do not cause sweating. Loss of body heat should be prevented without adding further heat. If person is fully conscious and not badly injured, lukewarm water may be given to allay thirst except in case of vomiting. Do not give stimulants. If medical aid is delayed and water is tolerated, add one half teaspoon salt and one half teaspoon baking soda to half-glass doses of water and give every fifteen minutes. Turn the head to one side if vomiting starts. Keep patient quiet, do not alarm and do not move unless absolutely necessary until the physician arrives.

Snake Bites (Poisonous). Keep patient quiet. Call for a doctor immediately. If bite is on an extremity, use anything that is available —necktie, belt, stocking or piece of shirt—to make a constricting band just above the bite. Keep the band just tight enough to slow the circulation, not stop it. If the swelling causes the band to get too tight, loosen it slightly. Make two incisions at right angles through each fang mark, using a sterilized razor blade or very sharp knife. The incisions should be about one-fourth inch long. Make shallow cuts crosswise, deeper cuts lengthwise, taking care to keep all cuts shallow on hands, wrists and top of feet. Using your mouth or suction cup, suck on the wound as strongly as possible. There is little danger of poisoning if your mouth is free of sores or scratches. As a precautionary measure, rinse the mouth after each suction. Keep the constricting band in place and continue suction over the incisions until medical attention is available. Work fast—maximum benefit from this suction occurs within first few minutes.

Splinters. Splinters of wood, glass or metal near the surface can usually be plucked out with a pair of tweezers, a needle or knife point. First apply an antiseptic to the wound, and sterilize the instrument used by passing it through a flame. After removing the splinter, it does no harm to cause a little bleeding by gentle pressure above the wound. This helps wash it out from the inside. Apply a sterile dressing or compress. Don't try to remove splinters that are buried deep in the flesh—have a doctor attend to it.

Sprains and Strains. Difficult to diagnose and treatments are different, so consult a physician promptly. Meanwhile, rest injured part.

Suffocation. Suffocation is a stoppage of breathing. It may be caused by electric shock, carbon monoxide poisoning, gas poisoning, drowning or strangulation. Get someone to call for emergency equipment immediately. Administer rescue breathing (see page 226) until help comes.

Unconsciousness. If cause is unknown, send for a doctor at once. If breathing has stopped or is very faint, begin artificial respiration at once. Place on abdomen and turn head to the side for easier breathing and to prevent aspiration of vomit. Never try to revive an unconscious person by shaking or slapping. Keep all parts immobile and use a stretcher or cot if transportation is necessary.

Bibliography

Pregnancy and Birth

Childbirth Without Fear, GRANTLY DICK READ, M.D., Harper & Brothers, 1959.

Expectant Motherhood, NICHOLSON J. EASTMAN, M.D., Little, Brown and Company, 1957.

Maternity: A Guide to Prospective Motherhood, FREDERICK W. GOODRICH, JR., M.D., Prentice-Hall, Inc., 1959.

Natural Childbirth, FREDERICK W. GOODRICH, JR., M.D., Prentice-Hall, Inc., 1950.

Pregnancy and Birth, ALAN F. GUTTMACHER, M.D., The Viking Press, 1957. Pocket reprint: (Signet Key) New American Library of World Literature, 1957.

Prenatal Care (pamphlet), Children's Bureau, U. S. Department of Health, Education, and Welfare, Washington, D.C., 1962.

Baby Care

Baby and Child Care, BENJAMIN SPOCK, M.D., Pocket Books, Inc., 1957. Revised version of: *The Common Sense Book of Baby and Child Care*, Duell, Sloan and Pearce, Inc., 1946.

Babies Are Human Beings, C. ANDERSON ALDRICH, M.D., and MARY M. ALDRICH, The Macmillan Company, 1954.

Feeding Your Child, SAMUEL M. WISHIK, M.D., Doubleday & Company, 1955.

Infant and Child in the Culture of Today, ARNOLD GESELL, M.D., and FRANCES L. ILG, M.D., Harper & Brothers, 1943.

Infant Care (pamphlet), Children's Bureau, U. S. Department of Health, Education, and Welfare, Washington, D.C., 1955.

Mother and Child, A Primer of First Relationships, D. W. WINNICOTT, M.D., Basic Books, Inc., 1957.

The Nursing Mother, FRANK HOWARD RICHARDSON, M.D., Prentice-Hall, Inc., 1953.

Preschool Child

Complete Book of Children's Play, RUTH E. HARTLEY, Ph.D., and ROBERT M. GOLDENSON, Ph.D., Thomas Y. Crowell Company, 1958.

Encyclopedia of Child Care and Guidance, SIDONIE MATSNER GRUENBERG, Doubleday & Company, Inc., 1954.

The Magic Years, SELMA H. FRAIBERG, Charles Scribner's Sons, 1959.

The Nursery School, KATHERINE H. READ, W. B. Saunders Company, 1960.

Teaching Your Child Right from Wrong, DOROTHY K. WHYTE, The Bobbs-Merrill Company, Inc., 1961.

Your Child from One to Six (pamphlet), Children's Bureau, U. S. Department of Health, Education, and Welfare, Washington, D.C., 1962.

Understanding Your Child, JAMES L. HYMES, JR., Prentice-Hall, Inc. 1952.

Index